Macrobiotic Seminars of Michio Kushi

Michio Kushi
Edited by Edward Esko

One Peaceful World Press
Becket, Massachusetts

Note to the Reader:

It is advisable for the reader to seek the guidance of a physician or other appropriate health care professional before implementing the approach to health suggested in this book. It is essential that any reader who has any reason to suspect serious illness contact a physician promptly. Neither this nor any other book should be used as a substitute for professional medical care or treatment.

Macrobiotic Seminars of Michio Kushi
Volume 1

For further information on mail-order sales, wholesale or retail discounts, distribution, translations, and foreign rights, please contact the publisher:

One Peaceful World Press
P.O. Box 10
Leland Road
Becket, MA 01223
U.S.A.

Telephone (413) 623-2322
Fax (413) 623-6042

First Edition: June 1998
10 9 8 7 6 5 4 3 2 1

ISBN 1–882984–29-3
Printed in U.S.A.

Contents

Introduction

Michio Kushi's teachings have inspired society for the last thirty-five years. Beginning with lectures in Boston in the 1960s and continuing with seminars around the United States and throughout the world in succeeding decades, he has introduced macrobiotics and principles of natural diet to thousands of people.

Many aspects of the modern health revolution can be traced to the early lectures that are included in this book. Today we take the connection between what we eat and our daily health for granted, but at the time this material was first presented, the major medical and scientific associations denied any direct connection between diet and degenerative disease, including cancer, heart disease, and others.

The articles in this volume are taken from a compiled edition of the *Order of the Universe*, a macrobiotic magazine published by Michio's students in Boston which has long been out of print. The Smithsonian Institution has recognized Michio's contribution to the health of modern society by gathering his papers and related macrobiotic materials for a permanent collection. This material is designed to be available to scholars and researchers, as well as the general public, and will be exhibited later this year.

In honor of that occasion, we are bringing out this special volume, which is a companion to *The Teachings of Michio Kushi* (One Peaceful World Press, 1993) and many other books by Michio Kushi that we have published in recent years (*see Bibliography*).

In an article published in the winter 1998 issue of the *One Peaceful World Journal*, Katherine Ott, an historian at the

Smithsonian, described the importance of the Kushi Collection in helping to "document the American experience":

> There are several reasons why we are interested in the Kushi macrobiotic materials. As a historian, I was trained to look for the big picture in small places: to analyze personal and local events in terms of national, global, and historical contexts. The macrobiotic movement is of historical importance because it intersects with many aspects of American life.
>
> I anticipate that in the future, scholars will come to the Smithsonian to use the Kushi materials in studying such things as the counter-culture of the 1960s; grass roots activist traditions; the rise of globalism and international relations; entrepreneurial businesses; food co-ops; peace studies; and American spiritual beliefs.
>
> Students of American foodways will find a broader context for understanding the growth of ethnic cuisine, the market in "exotic" foods, and the turn to natural whole foods which in turn affected agricultural practices. The materials are being stored in the Archives Center and in my division, Science, Medicine, and Society, which reflects my own interest in macrobiotics—that of the history of healing systems and medicine. And there are no doubt many other subjects we can not foresee today, for which researchers will come to study the Kushi materials.

We are happy to bring out this volume for a new generation and hope that it will contribute to health and happiness at many levels.

Alex Jack
Director, One Peaceful World
Becket, Mass.
January 3, 1998

1
Diagnosing Yourself

Please answer the following questions:

1. When your name is called, do you answer "Yes?" immediately and clearly? (If you do all the time, give yourself three points; if sometimes, two points; if hardly ever, one point.)

2. When the telephone rings, do you pick up the receiver and initiate the conversation? (If you do most of the time, three points; if sometimes, two points; if almost never, one point.)

3. When you come inside, do you take off your shoes and hang up your
coat? Or do you throw your clothes on the bed to be taken care of later? (If you take care of your clothes, three points; if you only take care of them occasionally, two points; if you hardly ever hang up your coat, one point.)

4. Do you turn off the lights when you don't want to use a room? (If the answer is "yes," give yourself three points; if you occasionally turn the lights off but often forget, two points; if you almost always forget, one point.)

5. Do you write immediate answers to the letters you receive? (If you reply on the same day you receive them, give yourself three points; if you wait a week or so, two points; if you take up to a month, one point.)

6. How many times must you clean yourself with paper after going to the toilet? (If one time, three points; if two

times, two points; if three times or more, one point.)

7. Can you enjoy any kind of game, without discrimination? (If you like most games, three points; if you like some but dislike others, two points; if you dislike most games, one point.)

8. How many friends do you have? (True friendship is unconditional and unlimited. If you have more than ten such friends, three points; if less than ten, two points; if only one or two, one point.)

9. How often do you become angry? (If only once a year, three points; if once a month, two points; if more than once a month, one point.)

10. When you are hungry, and there is nothing special prepared to eat, can you enjoy nothing but a simple meal of brown rice with gomashio or an umeboshi? (If you can always enjoy this, give yourself three points; if you wish that there were something else, two points; if you cannot enjoy it at all, one point.)

11. When you go out with friends to a restaurant or to a movie, do you manage to pay? (If you pay most of the time, three points; if fifty-fifty, like Dutch Treat, two points; if you hardly ever pay, one point.)

12. How many times did you change your work last year? (If you didn't change it or changed it only once, three points; if two points; if three times or more, one point.)

13. Do you like to keep your underwear clean? (If so, you get three points; if you sometimes do but sometimes forget, two points; if you usually forget, one point.)

14. Do you keep appointments? (If the answer is "Yes, most of the time," three points; if only sometimes, two points, if hardly ever, one point.)

15. When you see stars in the night, or, in the day, when you see leaves and flowers, do you feel "How wonderful?" (If you do, every time, three points; if sometimes, two points; if you don't care most of the time, one point.)

16. Do you like to travel? (If so, give yourself three points; if sometimes you enjoy travel but sometimes do not, two points; if you do not like to travel at all, one point.)

17. Do you like to read any kind of book? (If you do, take

three points; if you like some but dislike others, two points; if you do not like to read at all, one point.)

18. Do you have someone of the opposite sex whom you like very much? (Regardless of whether you have expressed this verbally, if there is such a person in your life, you should give yourself three points; if you are not sure, two points; if you almost never feel deep affection, one point.)

19. How long do you sleep? (If you sleep less than five hours per night, give yourself three points; if more than five hours, two points; if more than seven hours, one point.)

20. Whether your parents are alive or not, do you love and respect them very much? (If so, three points; if you sometimes do but sometimes do not, two points; if you think, "I don't like my parents very much," one point or zero.)

21. Do you have a humorous expression, and do you use it often? (If so, three points; if only sometimes, two points; if you are not so humorous, one point.)

22. Do you have nightmares? (If you never have nightmares, three points; if you seldom do, two points; if you have nightmares often, one point.)

23. For women: Do you menstruate regularly? (If you menstruate every twenty-eight days, give yourself three points; if you are fairly regular, two points; if you are not so regular, one point.)

For men: Do you like exercise, sports, or any kind of physical activity? (If you like these things very much, three points; if you sometimes like them but sometimes do not, two points; if you do not like them at all, one point.)

24. When you finish a meal, do you often leave leftovers on your dish? (If you eat everything, three points; if you occasionally leave something, two points; if you leave something, one point.)

25. Do you often say "Thank you," or "Thank you very much?" (If you express your thanks often, ten, twenty, or thirty times per day, give yourself three points; if you say "Thank you" less than ten times per day, two points; if you almost never give thanks, one point or zero.)

Add your points to find your score.

75: Highest possible score. Either you are the happiest person in the world or the most arrogant person. If you have a perfect score, you have nowhere to go but down.

65 or more: You are happy now, even though you may not be aware of it.

55-64: You will be happy within one year (as long as you are eating well).

45-54: You will be happy within two years.

35-44: You will be happy within three years.

35 or less: In the future you will become the happiest person.

If your score is low, and you have two or three years to become happy, or if it is very low, you have the potential to become the happiest person in the future. Your qualifications are therefore very good to enter our school.

2
The Way of Life

We are children of the atomic age, the culmination of centuries of technological development. One cannot help but be impressed by the wonders that modern science has produced in the last few decades. And yet there is something lacking in our rapid development. Despite scientific gains, we have still failed to solve the fundamental problems of humanity.

Enormous stockpiles of nuclear weapons have not brought us any closer to world peace. The ability to conquer many bacteria and lower the infant mortality rate has not eliminated the great degenerative diseases, such as cancer and heart disease. Mental illness is quickly becoming an even greater problem than the "physical" diseases. The divorce rate and the increasing use of drugs and alcohol indicate that modern people are dissatisfied. Although we are the most advanced, best educated people in history, we are powerless to find practical solutions to the problems of peace, health, and happiness. There is something basically wrong with the modern way of life.

The way of life that we are presenting is a little different from the way that most of the modern world is taking. Instead of complexity, we offer simplicity; abandoning the artificial, we stress the natural; instead of the analytical, we offer the universal. Our purpose is to unite scientific knowledge of the physical and technical world with the intuitive knowledge of the universe that humanity once enjoyed. The synthesis of these antagonistic, yet complementary ways of life can bring about a true Golden Age of humanity.

Many great thinkers detect that humanity has reached a very critical point in its long history. The choice of direction is completely up to us. Whether we realize it or not, our destiny is in our own hands. Changes take place today more rapidly than at any time in history. Modern methods of communication and transportation permit new ideologies to spread throughout the world in a matter of months, instead of centuries. A nuclear war could be fought in less than an hour. Our hope for a new world is a great and very possible dream.

We are grateful to have been born into this age, and accept its great problems with excitement, for it offers a greater challenge and potential for development and fulfillment than any time in history. In our lectures, we examine modern society and suggest an embracing view of life that can bring unity out of chaos. We offer, as encouragement, a new understanding of ancient cosmologies that have been forgotten or misunderstood. This is the unifying principle, a simple, yet universally applicable conception of the order of the universe, for the way of life in the age of humanity.

3
The Seasons of the Galaxy

Let us observe our Milky Way galaxy through the magic spectacles of our imagination. We know that life started on our planet about 3. 2 billion years ago, and that our solar system is revolving around the center of the galaxy in a cycle that lasts 200 million years. Since the beginning of life, then, our solar system has made about sixteen turns around the center of the galaxy. Ten revolutions ago, bacteria came out and slowly developed into fish; only two revolutions ago, in the Late Paleozoic Era, the first amphibians were formed. One revolution ago (about two hundred million years ago) giant ferns covered the earth.

We observe the cycle of the universe in our daily lives. We are a little hungry; then we become ravenous. We eat a little, and become fairly satisfied; finally we are full, and we stop. The cycle begins again. We change from a child, to a youth, to an adult, to old age. The day, the seasons—everything follows the same general pattern. Small yang changes into great yang; great yang changes into small yin; small yin changes into great yin; great yin changes into small yang once again. Between the two extremes of winter and summer, or midnight and noon, there are always the milder periods of autumn and spring, or morning and evening.

Our Milky Way has four seasons, just as our earth does. Of course, the orbit would not be perfectly balanced—nothing is! Through the revolutions that it has undergone so far, then, many changes have taken place. Hot and cold periods have alternated to bring about many different living conditions. Ferns developed in galactic winter; they contracted, forcing the leaves to split into many sections. Then, in the spring, they began to expand and cover the earth. About this time, too, giant reptiles and dinosaurs developed under the expansive influence of warm weather. Many species were produced during this time of diversification (yin). About 63 million years ago, as the galaxy moved into autumn, the huge trees began to die, along with the large animals. The cold weather demanded different forms of life; herbs, grasses, and grains came out, and mammals started. The first of four glacial periods began.

Animal life is dependent, directly or indirectly, upon vegetable life. Animals evolved, or changed, by eating the changed foods that were available to them. Our ancient ancestors became human by eating the grains that had begun to grow. About thirty million years ago, the ancestors of humanity developed. Humanity, then, is a product of the autumn season of the Milky Way. We can see how our own activity changes during the year; our physical nature is dominant during the summer, while sexuality reaches a peak in the spring. The galactic seasons are similar; spring saw the differentiation of many species, summer their physical development, and autumn, which is usually the time we think best, their intellectual development.

Now we are entering galactic winter. Humanity's living space during this period may be small, and we may become shorter. We can live comfortably, however, once we learn the order of eating, the means to balance our constitution with our environment through proper selection of food and proper cooking. This is the key to humanity's future development, and this century will decide whether or not we grasp it. If we do, we can live continuously through all four seasons of the galaxy.

4
Spirals

Distant galaxies revolve, a moth spins into light, water swirls down a drain, hair grows. What do these have in common? They seem to be fairly unrelated until we realize that all of them move in spirals. Everything around us is in motion, changing constantly, and when we realize this our first impression is often one of confusion and bewilderment. There seems to be no order or direction. When we look closer, however, we begin to understand the way things change, and we see spiral movement everywhere—in plants, animals, atoms, stars, and in our lives. The spiral is the pattern of the universe.

The first created thing is a spiral, and everything else in the world comes from this. In order to picture this, let us imagine our origin, or cosmological will, as infinite expanding movement, branching outward endlessly. When two streams of movement collide, they curl inward. As the motion approaches the center, it becomes denser, and matter is formed. Matter is produced from non-matter! There is no sharp distinction between the two—just the smooth continuum of the spiral. We are made in the same way, by a process of materialization. Our body is a contraction from infinity.

Contraction and expansion, or yang and yin, are the laws that govern the spiral. Distinctions, relative differences, are found within the spiral, but this itself is a part of infinity. We can reach the infinite by passing through the gates of yin and yang, that is to say, by studying relativity. Having reached the center of a spiral to become human, we must expand outward, broadening our view until it includes everything.

The first spiral of created matter makes the world of preatomic elements. The movement of these again produces spirals, which form electrons, the first particles of the world of elements. An electron, in turn, enters a spiral and changes into a proton when it reaches the center. The first, simplest element, hydrogen, is formed of one electron and one proton. All other elements are formed from this, by transmutation—a process that is going on all around us, at every instant. Electrons and protons are not particles, but huge galaxies, and each "particle" within the galaxy is itself another galaxy. There is no absolute, final particle of matter upon which everything is based. Spirals can be traced infinitely in all directions. Our sensory perceptions discover one section of this infinite scale, but we can perceive its entire depth with our intuition.

The solar system is also a spiral, formed, as always, from

the outside. A planet is drawn into the spiral and moves slowly toward the sun, on a journey that takes billions of years. It changes constantly, acquiring and losing moons, growing and diminishing, altering the position of its axis many times. Finally it reaches the position of Mercury, begins to burn, and falls into the sun. Some scientists predict that the sun will burn itself out without realizing that it is constantly being refueled!

As we move upward in scale, spirals become more evident. The smaller, more compacted spirals, are difficult to detect, because their rate of change is very slow by our standard. It takes billions of years for an electron to reach the center of a spiral, and even with our present sophisticated scientific instruments, we cannot measure the change in the earth's orbit as it moves toward the sun.

Spirals become more yin as the scale increases, so that we can easily detect the construction of a galaxy. Our own Milky Way is a spiral, about 75 billion light years across, and our solar system is one speck among thousands that make up its curves. If our vision were large enough, we could see that universes, too are spirals, and that this unfolding pattern continues—in all imaginable directions.

The marks of our origin are everywhere—in the cowlick on the back of our head, the whorls of our fingertips, in the shape of our organs. The human body is formed in a spiral—the "mortal coil" that Shakespeare referred to. Our lives, too, form spiral patterns of contraction and expansion, give and take, materialization and spiritualization. Many ancient people worshipped spirals, painting them on their temples and monuments. How wonderful they are! With them, we can find the order of the universe.

5
Developing Endless Gratitude

In the Orient everyone knows we have two kinds of eyes; the eyes of the body (Niku-Gan), and the eyes of the mind (Shin-Gan). The first can see only bodily objects, but when you develop the latter you can see the invisible aspects of everything. These eyes can see the whole world, past and future, on an infinite scale. They can perceive beginningless infinity to endless infinity, as well as the meaning of our present state. This is the reason for our way of eating—to develop our Shin-Gan. As you follow the way of eating, you will find that your daily life is becoming less and less attached to material things, and you will begin to discover these worlds of invisibility.

If you do not open these eyes, your life will become very unhappy and narrow; but when you do, this earth will become a smaller and smaller point in the cosmos, until finally you can free yourself completely. Zazen, or sitting meditation, was developed to cultivate this vision, but the most basic, fundamental method is the way of eating, for this changes the quality of billions of cells which determine our thinking, acting, and perceiving.

Once you begin to feel this, you will discover the world of On. This is a Japanese word made up of the characters for "origin" and "mind." It is the most basic principle of the Oriental mentality. On is an attitude—a way of thinking that always searches for the cause and origin of everything, and seeks to repay many times what has been given. Of course, we cannot see the origin of things until our inner vision has been opened. A person with On feels deep, unlimited thanks for everything—parents, teachers, society, nations, the sun, water, soil, the galaxy, the universe, ancestors, sickness, difficulties—especially difficulties.

In Japan there is an expression which illustrates On very well: "On of one bowl of rice and one night." We can picture a tired, hungry traveler, who meets someone who offers him food and lodging. "I don't have any fine food," the host explains, "just a bowl of rice—I hope it's enough." When it is time to go to bed, he explains that he has no blanket, but, "Please make yourself at home anywhere on the floor—I'm sorry I can't do better." In the morning the traveler goes on his way, with the "On of one bowl of rice and one night." This means that for the rest of his life he will try to repay what has been given him, that he will be eternally grateful to his new friend. On is the life of a person who understands the permanency and consistency of infinity, and the inconsistency of infinite change. It has nothing to do with give and take, or with concepts of right and obligation.

Such words were absent from the Oriental vocabulary until Western ideas began to penetrate. They were translated as "Kenri" (authority to gain profit) for "right," and "Gimu" (burden) for "obligation." After these words were coined, modern laws began to be based on them. Earlier, this concept of "give and take" was entirely unnecessary, and it is completely incompatible with On. If someone gave, it was natural for the receiver to try to give back more—infinitely. Without On, man is nothing more than a beast.

Oriental thought divides humanity into seven categories. The "Gaki," or "hungry devil," doesn't think of others at all; he just takes and takes, eats and eats. He could hardly even be called a man. The next is the "Chikusho," or "domesticated beast." Most employees belong to this group, as do many members of educational institutions. They complain, yet they continue to follow. Lacking self-discipline, they allow others to regulate their lives. Here is a coffee break, there is the holiday—they live in a state of slavery from moment to moment. The "Dorei," or "slaves," are not necessarily slaves to others; they are also slaves to their own concepts and desires.

The "Hito" is the first true man. His ideogram means "yin and yang supporting each other." He begins to know order, but he still does not know what justice is nor does he have the wisdom to know himself. The "Kenjin" or "man of wisdom," begins to know himself, he discerns the proper direction. The "Seijin" or "holy man," is a saint. His sign includes the ideograms for "ear" and "mouth." In other words, he can freely control what he hears and what he says. He can solve social problems, and this is a very high development, indeed.

The highest man, however, is beyond sainthood. This is the "Jiyujin" or "free man." A literal translation means, simply, "self" or "mountain man." They were reputed to live on roots and mist and dew, spending their days flying where they wanted to go and changing anything they liked as their play. Often they lived for hundreds of years.

The higher one goes, the less company there is. The distribution could be charted on a pyramid. The majority are always at the lower levels, and free men are almost nonexistent. Political leaders are usually found in the third and fourth categories, while thinkers and philosophers range up to the sixth. What type of government is best? As we can see, democracy is inevitably based on the will of people with low judgment. The ideal government would be administered by a Jiyujin—but how could he be brought out? Would the masses ask him to govern? There is an Oriental proverb that says, "The true man is always there, but no one can find him."

The best way, then, is to develop yourself. Establish your own happiness before anything else. Discover this amazing principle of On: "One grain, ten thousand grains." Just as one grain of rice multiplies itself a thousand fold, give back many times what you were given. This is the basic condition of happiness. Practice it from today, and you will find that your daily life is becoming happier day by day.

6
Why Did We Become Human?

We came to this earth by changing ourselves from infinity, traveling a spiral path from the seventh to the first heaven. From infinity, we separated into yin and yang; then we became vibrations, pre-atomic particles, elements, vegetables, and animals, finally emerging as a human being. In the seventh heaven there was no schizophrenia, no illness, no irregular menstruation, war, or suffering of any kind. Illness does not start until we reach the world of vegetables; it is a very small, almost insignificant problem in the universe as a whole. The world of man has lying, poverty, confusion—it is nothing but hell.

Why have we come from heaven to hell?

Our Milky Way galaxy revolves at 300 kilometers per second. It takes about 200 million years for our solar system to make a complete orbit around the center of the galaxy. We live on the second orbit from the outside; about two-thirds of the distance from galactic center. Our stay here has only taken a small fragment of one revolution, a tiny angle. Why did you abandon the oneness of infinity and differentiate yourself into billions of people, fighting and attacking one another? Such difficulties to be overcome make for much excitement. But did you come only to seek excitement? Within this world of conflict and war you are seeking peace. Is it possible?

Siva, the God of Happiness

In India, 4,000 years ago, Vedanta philosophy developed and began to spread, eventually becoming our present-day Buddhism and Hinduism. The highest concept of this ancient philosophy was the idea of the God of Happiness, or Siva. In Japan, this was re-interpreted into practical applications concerning biological and physiological problems of longevity. The word "Siwa" came to mean both "happiness" and "wrinkles," such as the marks on the face and the palms of the hands. Saiwaism arose in the fourth century as a way of pursuing happiness. This idea, with its anthropological origins in the Middle East, is a wonderful expression of our true direction. We are all seeking Saiwai. Today, people do not even know what the word "happiness" can mean. Siva's wife was Kali, the Goddess of Happiness, and Calcutta was named after her. Today, this "capital of happiness" is riddled by beggars. Our direction has been lost.

Until supreme judgment, whatever you try to do, fails. This is hell. Most die before reaching this point; very few discover this happy life. Hell is the world of the mentally abnormal, the domain of sick people. In the domain of the free person, there is nothing but playing, every day. There is no concept of sickness, government, nationality, or titles. If you think you are happy in the lower world, you will find that it vanishes later. In the higher world, there is only present tense—no past or future, no gender, and no Buddha, Jesus, God, soul, spirit, philosophy, or unifying principle. At this point you detach yourself from all learnings, including food disciplines. All doctrines, including the greatest, such as those of Lao Tsu, are necessary only for the lower worlds. When you graduate, you make them your friends, and play with them. Distinctions between "student" and "teacher" vanish.

Raising Our Judgment

The higher we go, the less arrogance we have. When a person reaches the intellectual level, he or she starts to develop social judgment, or a view of the world. Until this point, concepts of good and bad, just and unjust, morality, and God, are necessary. The highest judgment accomplishes a view of the cosmos—and then forgets about it.

We are always transmuting the invisible into the visible. We change our dream into an image, and our image, into material reality. When our judgment is lower, we fail to accomplish this again and again. When we reach the highest judgment, we can make our thinking straight and clear, and go directly to our goal. If everyone were to reach supreme judgment, there would be no more sickness, difficulties, or troubles; people could live a very long time.

Proper eating accelerates our development millions of years. There are no prohibitions; we eat everything, freely, according to the order of the universe. As we eat outward on the spiral of creation we develop higher and higher. When we are in our mother's womb, we eat the essence of animal food—blood. After we are born, we continue to eat animal food in the form of mother's milk, however, after we have eaten there, we arrest our growth at this point if we continue basing our diet on animal foods. Grains and vegetables enable us to continue to go outward, so that we expand our view more and more until we identify ourselves with the entire universe. Grains and vegetables, to become human, give themselves up as food. By eating them our judgment develops upward.

We eat elements in the form of water and salt, pre-atomic particles as the fire we use to cook our food, and we take in vibrations as sound, light, and the world of yin and yang—the gateway to the infinite. Starting at the center of the spiral, we eat outward until we embrace the whole universe. There is no division between the worlds of material reality and spirituality; they form a continuum on the spiral. The farther out we go, the more we encounter the spiritual. We can determine our existence and perceptions, then, by controlling what we eat. When we fast, for instance, we eat farther outward on the spiral and thus understand more of truth and justice.

Why Eat Well?

Over the past ten years, many of our friends have begun to eat grains and vegetables. Most of them have realized that this is good food, and feel that as long as they eat this way nothing more is necessary to grasp the order of the universe. Such people are called fools. They don't know why we should eat good food, they don't see beyond this one application of the unifying principle. They do not realize that good food is nothing but the fundamental means to establish our health. At least 70 percent of our friends think the biological application of yin and yang is enough.

Among the remaining 30 percent, most realize that this way of eating has given them health, reduced their medical expenses, and they feel that they have, therefore, graduated. These people are called crazy. Health isn't the target, but the fundamental means to achieve freedom. There are many kinds of freedom—material, social, ideological, the freedom of life itself—and once they have accomplished these, they graduate themselves. Only a small percentage, perhaps 8 percent or so, try to gain this. If they consider their mission accomplished, as most do, they are called mad. Freedom is not our target—it is the entrance to happiness.

Out of the few that seek freedom, about one-ninth find what they really are and secure their own happiness. These are called ignorant. Happiness is nothing but the beginning of an eternal realization of an endless dream. Endless depth, infinity itself—this is happiness. When you reach this, you will realize just how wonderful our unifying principle is. After you become happy, your real life starts. Until this you have not been born as a free human being. Ninety-nine percent of people are not born until their death. Our real life starts from this point.

Originally, we had this happiness. What happened? Where did we fail? If we had not lost our direction, we could enjoy life on this planet without any trouble. We could live for centuries, as the Bible relates. Each living cell, if given the proper environment, can live endlessly. Alexis Carrel, in his excellent book *Man, The Unknown*, tells of an experiment he performed with the heart of a chicken. When he removed it and cultivated it carefully, it lived seven times longer than an ordinary chicken's heart! In France, a General's grave, which had been sealed at the time of Napoleon, was opened so that the body could be removed. The beard of the man had continued growing for 200 years, until it was longer than his body! Near Madagascar, a big fish was found which was supposed to have been extinct for several millions of years. Do you see the possibilities for life that we are missing? It is our own choices that limit us.

What is God?

So many thinkers have come and gone. Do we know any more about God because of them? Here are a few of their conclusions:

Kant: "God is supreme reason."
Hamilton: "God is eternally unknown."

Schopenhauer: "God is will."
Bergson: "God is life energy."
Lipps: "God is consciousness."
Bradley: "God is full experience."
Alexander: "God is the maker of time and space and everything."
Hegel: "God is the universal spirit."

This is the cream of human wisdom! What do you think of it? We must conclude that humanity's greatest thinkers know nothing of God. Their statements may be summarized, simply:

1. "I don't know God," or
2. "God is somewhere—so, I believe." In other words, "I don't know, so I believe." This is "faith." Faith of this sort equals superstition; it is nothing but the other side of ignorance. This is the way of the saint, and it inevitably creates slaves. Even Buddha made this mistake.

Another technique is to ignore the problem altogether and to try to overpower the world, nature, ourselves. This is the way of the Pharisees, or scientists. Both ways end in unhappiness, either as (1) the servant of God, or (2) the servant of demons.

Here is our way: We say that our body, which we created, is an infinitesimal point in our larger, real Self. This Self = God. Our real Self is eternal, immortal. We make both "God" and "demon" our servants. We take this as our great adventure, the realization of our dream. Here is our definition of "adventure":

$$\text{Adventure} = \frac{(x)^2}{(\text{exclusivity})}$$

As you can see, this is similar to Newton's formula for gravity; our adventure increases as our exclusivity diminishes. For exclusivity you may substitute "attachment." As you become less attached, your life increases.

7
Basic Acupuncture

Our body takes food from every level of the spiral of creation. We eat animal food (mother's blood), vegetables, elements, all the way to vibrations. We take electromagnetic energy, or Ki, from the atmosphere around us. The ancient Chinese studied this, and discovered that there are tiny points all over our body that receive this energy, distributed along lines that transverse the body. These tiny "mouths" are formed in spirals under the surface of the skin, and are connected by tiny passageways. From this knowledge they developed the finest symptomatic medicine—acupuncture.

There are about 365 points connected by fourteen lines; twelve of them, corresponding to the twelve constellations, are connected to the twelve major organs. (More yin organs and functions are: the stomach, bladder, small intestine, large intestine, triple heater, and gallbladder. More yang organs and functions are: the spleen/pancreas, kidneys, heart, lungs, heart governor, and liver. Please try to match yin organs with yang organs and classify the organ pairs from most yin to most yang.) The months of the year, the hours on our clock, and the Oriental calendar all operate on a cycle of twelve, corresponding to the movement of the galaxy and constellations. The two remaining lines, running down the center of the body, coordinate the others. These are known as the governing and conception vessels. When an organ is functioning poorly the corresponding points will become hard and sensitive, and the proper organ can be treated by stimulating the sore point.

The old Chinese sages decided to use these channels to treat disease. They developed methods to influence the organs as they wished: needles (tiny pins inserted in the proper places), moxa burning (a special herb ignited on the spot to be affected), and simple pressure stimulation. The later is known as *Shiatsu*. It is very effective and may be used by anyone without an overly detailed knowledge of acupuncture.

These techniques have been used to effect quite miraculous recoveries. They are still very popular in the Orient as a traditional medicine. Interestingly enough, this ancient discovery has continued to escape the analytical methods of modern science. When the Chinese found these points, they were looking from their cosmological point of view, from the whole to the part. When we begin with the whole, we can find everything; when we search microscopically, we are limited to merely partial success, which is failure.

The ancient sages could do many seemingly miraculous things that modern science cannot explain. Recently, a 3,000 year old tomb was unearthed; analysis showed it to be composed of a 95 percent aluminum—5 percent copper alloy. How could they do this? Even with our modern knowledge, we didn't make aluminum until fifty years ago! There are very old pagodas that stand without any central support; a pole hangs from the top which stops just before touching the ground. These have stood through centuries of earthquakes. How did they do this?

What wisdom ancient people had! The quality of their brain was very different from our modern mentality. Why? Because they ate whole grains as their main food. How clear their thinking was because of this! They used yin and yang to describe all of the lines and points and make unifying theories that explained their operation. If we want to heal ourselves, this is the only fundamental method. Acupuncture is limited, and its results can only be temporary as long as we continue to eat improperly. Many European doctors have begun to use these methods, and they are accepted by the official medicine of France. If we can combine acupuncture with proper eating, we can rediscover the real freedom enjoyed by these ancient people. We can play as they did—without money, weapons, or complicated facilities, and can build, achieve, and enjoy our life.

8
Surviving Emergencies

World War II ended in the summer of 1945 when the atomic bomb was dropped on Hiroshima and Nagasaki. In Hiroshima, almost 350,000 people were destroyed immediately. Out of a population of 500,000, 70 percent were killed at once, and many buildings were destroyed completely. Nuclear war is a constant threat in our age. Is there anything we can do about it?

Sometimes we receive advice through the mail urging us to build fallout shelters in the basement and giving simple instructions. Very simple calculations show that such defenses would be almost completely ineffective against atomic destruction. Of course, they could be slightly helpful, but we must remember that today's weapons are hundreds and thousands of times more powerful than those dropped on Hiroshima and Nagasaki. If one of these were to explode over our cities, these barricades would be useless, except in a very few cases. If you were protected by a hill from the air pressure, you might have a chance, but the force of a direct explosion would probably render the shelter useless.

What happens in an atomic explosion? First, there is a brilliant flash of light. When they were testing the atomic bomb in the South Pacific, some Japanese fishermen were near, although outside the danger area. When they saw the light, they cried, "The sun! The sun is rising from the West!"

Next there is heat. If you are close to this, it is very intense. In Hiroshima the shadows of those who experienced the direct force of this heat were baked to the buildings. An entire regiment of soldiers was completely reduced to ashes. At first, no one noticed. One soldier, who was sick had been confined to sick bay, felt something like an earthquake and was forced to crawl out of a collapsed building. When he finally reached the sunlight, he saw his friends standing, and began to inch toward them, shouting for help. When he finally reached one and touched him, the soldier collapsed. The intense heat had changed him to standing ashes.

Pressure comes next, destroying most buildings, followed by radioactivity and fallout. The latter covers the whole earth. A bomb dropped in Seattle will completely deluge New England with radioactivity. Although it is invisible, it must be completely cleansed from the skin at once if severe sickness is to be avoided. With soap, it can be removed to a certain extent. The symptoms of this modern plague, which struck the Japanese fishermen who witnessed the early explosions, begin with general fatigue, followed by loss of all hair. Eventually, you begin to vomit blood, while fatigue increases until vitality has completely vanished. Finally, internal organs swell, white blood cells decrease, and many abnormal symptoms appear until the disease culminates in death. Even today, there are many survivors of Hiroshima who are dying from atomic disease. Of course, the effect of fallout is not limited to direct attack on our skin; it infiltrates the oceans and the rivers which run deep under the earth and finally begins to invade our vegetables. All of our nourishment, including fish and animals, could possibly become contaminated by fallout.

Radioactivity, being very expansive, is extremely yin. In order to survive fallout, then, your condition must be very good. If you are yang and not too close to the blast, you have a great chance to survive. If you are taking chemicalized foods, citrus fruits, etc., every day, you are yin, and you will immediately attract the yang forces of light, heat, and pressure, and be destroyed immediately. If you have been eating animal quality yang food, you cannot survive radioactivity very easily. Vegetable food, however, enables one to survive atomic danger, if it is not too direct, but it should not be the usual "vegetarian" food of fruits and raw vegetables. Eating well-cooked grains and vegetables as the main food gives the best condition for survival.

There are many stories which illustrate this. In Nagasaki, there were two hospitals situated equidistant from the blast. In one of them, everyone was killed; in another, 100 percent of the staff and patients survived, except for one minister from the West. This was St. Francis Hospital, a chronic ward where patients had been kept for a long time. Since it was a Catholic hospital, the Japanese people called this event "the miracle of Nagasaki." The director of this hospital was a man named Dr. Akizuki, who is now around 65 years of age. He and his assistants were serving everyone in the hospital a diet of well-cooked grains and vegetables. After the explosion, they carried bags of brown rice from the basement, although fallout was still in the air. Behind hastily erected shelters they cooked rice, with sea salt, miso soup, and deep-fried pumpkin, for several days, until the rescue operations finally reached them. Like Dr. Akizuki, many of these people are still living today.

In an emergency, the final decisions of our survival depend entirely on what we eat. Our food determines our biological constitution.

Here is another example. In the last war, a boat, carrying 3,000 soldiers across the Pacific, was attacked by an American submarine and began to sink. Some, who could not swim, died immediately. Others called to each other and sang, to keep each other's spirits up, but finally were overcome by the waves and approaching darkness. In the morning, no more than a hundred were left, and these were widely scattered. When a cruiser came, only a very few of the remaining could be helped. Eight of the soldiers managed to reach an island, but four of them died immediately. Three of these passed away in the next few days. The sole survivor spent a month on the island, and was finally rescued. This man, one out of three thousand, had been eating grains and vegetables.

In the city of Yokohama, a fire broke out at Sakurage Station, on the elevated urban transit line. Vehicular and pedestrian traffic became jammed as hundreds watched the flames spread over the train which had been stopped over Sakurage Street, completely unable to help the people crying for help from the windows. The train and all of its passengers were destroyed, except for one eighteen year-old boy.

This boy was a student of George Ohsawa, and he had been eating grains and vegetables for some time. Because his health was good and his intuition was keen, he felt that something was wrong long before anyone realized there was a fire.

When the train stopped he tried to open the window but found it locked. While he was waiting, shouts began several cars away, and he finally broke the window and climbed out, slipping down to the side. Since the train was elevated, there was nowhere to go. Hanging on carefully, he crawled from window to window and managed to escape. Soon thereafter, the fire became evident. Everyone tried to leave at once, and in the struggle, confusion, and noise, all were killed.

There are so many examples like these. In an emergency, who can save you? No one but yourself. Your physiological, biological, and psychological condition will be the only possible means of rescue. How you detect the threat, how you react, how you escape, all depend on your condition. If you are eating poorly, you will be crushed. Whether it is an accident or an atomic war, your judgment and your quality will be tested. When reports come that nuclear warheads are coming, it is too late to begin to eat well. Let us begin to prepare ourselves, now, in everyday life, for any kind of emergency.

9
Ancient Government

Confucius and Lao Tsu lived in a time of constant wars and intrigue. In their teachings they referred to the three dynasties that came before theirs, which they considered the Golden Age of China. Being acquainted with history, they knew that humanity had degenerated. The Chou Dynasty came directly before theirs. It was a peaceful time which produced the Book of Change and other classics. Before this there were the legendary times of Fu Hi (the author of yin and yang), the Yellow Emperor, and of the three emperors Gyo, Shun, and Wu. These emperors did not give their kingdom to their children; they searched for someone who would be most suitable. In these ideal times, the emperor's palace was very small, just like an ordinary home, and his governmental duties were very small. Only a few clerical workers were necessary to manage the whole empire. There were very few regulations and laws, and these were extremely simple. There were no grand armies, no police, and no hospitals.

Behind these emperors were consultants. These advisors were known as Sennin. They were hidden, their names unknown. They did not necessarily live in the mountains. Sometimes they were in the town, living as ordinary men, but they were very wise. Especially well remembered are the "Seven Wise Men of the Bamboo Forest." These sages, all seventy or eighty years of age, lived happily in a grove, and when the emperor was perplexed he would consult with them. Because of these Sennin, the government could run. They did not do any clerical work, but when necessary, they directed the country's future.

The judgment of these men was considered higher than that of a saint. A saint is antagonistic to immoral, criminal, and evil people. The Sennin embraced everything; they could understand the good, saintly person, together with the evil. These kind of people were living in ancient Japan as well as China, lending ideological, philosophical and spiritual backing to the government. They were called "people above the clouds." Later, this name was used for the ordinary nobles and administrators.

This kind of system was used in the West as well as the Orient. In the Old Testament, for instance, we read of prophets; these people gave advice to the king. The first king of Israel, Saul, consulted with Samuel, who also helped the next king, David. Samuel, Daniel, and other wise men, would be near the kings, giving ideas and judgment. Sometimes they would be against the king's and the people's opinions, and they would give warnings. For example, when Israel was first formed as a country, and the first king was chosen, Samuel bitterly opposed such a system. The people wanted a king, but he told them many times, that they would become the king's servants, losing their sons to his armies and their money to his taxes. Since the people insisted, he was finally compelled to choose a king.

In ideal government, ideological and political problems become one. In ancient times, with this system, ideal government could be realized. About 3,000 years ago, however, throughout East and West, this kind of government decayed, and emperors became political leaders, without great advisors behind the curtains. Since then, there have been no Sennin. A few remain here and there, living private lives, but they are not involved directly in the problems of the people. It is quite possible, for example, that some may be living in the Himalayan Mountains, but they are not a part of Indian politics.

These Sennin were very different from the present-day political consultants. The Kennedy cabinet had many scholars and scientists as advisors, a very admirable method in modern politics, but this is very different from the ancient system, in which the people behind the curtain were persons of supreme judgment and universal consciousness. The nearest example in our modern world is the teacher and advisor of Mao Tse-tung. This man, nearly eighty, is not a Communist at all, but a very deep thinker, an Oriental philosopher. He is very free; he can go anywhere, but when he is needed, he is called and consulted. This is the only person Mao Tse-tung kneels down before.

The Sennin disappeared 3,000 years ago. Now is the time when these people of supreme judgment will appear and give advice, warnings or consultations, for practical economic or political problems. You may see this happening very soon. Perhaps some will come from our friends.

10
Waves and Particles

Recently, three astronauts returned to the earth after eleven days of space travel. According to our present schedule, we will send a man to the moon by the middle of next year. These rapid strides in space exploration will become more and more rapid in the future. Perhaps our attention will be drawn to the moon, the planets, and space, and away from our trifling problems. Let us hope a thousand flying saucers come.

Today, we would like to invite you to a very interesting world, in connection with this space. Think very carefully; when we see each other, we are seeing in space, but in present space. Our comprehension of past and future is not developed enough. We detect objects in relation to each other, but we often miss this depth of time. Our senses are very defective in this respect. For past and future, we must use a different instrument, such as imagination, inspiration, or intuition.

Actually, everything is like this. Since we are seeing only the surface, one moment of time in space, we often see only one side, and fail to comprehend the whole. If we add the dimension of time, we can see that everything has both a wave character and a particle character.

There are many questions still unsolved in connection with light. Einstein, for instance, decided that light travels at a constant speed, and is the fastest thing in the universe. It was from this hypothesis that he began to develop his cosmology. His opinion has continued to influence the scientific world so strongly that it is still assumed that the speed of light is constant and unchanging.

According to our unifying principle, there is nothing that is constant. If you admit this big principle, that nothing remains the same, that everything changes, forever, then the speed of light should also change. Which do we accept?

According to Einstein, light remains the same whether we measure it here or a hundred, or a billion miles away. Let us examine this. Here is our sun; light starts here, and travels in the depths of space. If your intuition tells you that the speed changes, would you think it becomes faster or slower as it travels outward?

First, we must see yin and yang. The sun, the source of brightness, is very yang, while space, darkness, is very yin. As light penetrates farther into darkness, would it become faster or slower? The farther it went, the greater the attraction would be, and the faster it would travel. Finally, what would happen? The speed would become infinite. At this point, it could not be seen, and it would become darkness.

The darkness of this universe is moving with infinite or nearly infinite velocity. The sun is matter; matter changes into light, which changes into infinite expansion. Everything on our earth, including human beings, eventually changes into these enormous currents of moving space. If there was no great movement within darkness, it could not give birth to new stars and galaxies.

About four hundred years ago, a new star was born. This was recorded in Japanese and Chinese history. In the Orient, these are called "guest stars," having recently arrived as compared to the "main," or "host" stars. New stars are being born constantly, while old ones are fading away. Brightness changes into darkness, and darkness into brightness, yang changes into yin, yin changes into yang. Of course, there is much movement in this active brightness, but in the darkness, even more change is going on, with higher speeds. In other words, great yin has great yang. Darkness appears very still and silent, but this is only the front. The great back of darkness is immense and infinite speed and change, greater than that found in brightness. The change in brightness is visible; that in darkness, we cannot see. We must see it with our imagination, our insight.

Light

The nature of light is one of the biggest problems of science. There have been many opinions advanced, and, through countless experiments, it has finally been determined that light has two different characters. Sometimes, it acts like particles; sometimes, like waves. This is very peculiar, isn't it? Scientists are very confused, and cannot comprehend this paradox. Light is waves, but at the same time, particles. This is very, very difficult to conceive.

In high school, we studied the solar system: the sun, surrounded by planets moving in neatly fixed elliptical orbits. This concept is a dead, frozen view, not the living solar system that actually exists. If we add the dimension of time, we see that it is moving, as a whole, and our understanding changes. It is as if we cut a tree and studied the rings that form its cross-section. We can understand its structure by doing this, but we have no idea of its height and growth. We must see the whole tree in order to understand its history. The top of the tree stump resembles a miniature solar system; if we study only this one section, our view remains fixed.

The picture of the solar system, frozen on the pages of the textbook, is only momentary. When we watch a motion picture, we see a very interesting story, but if we remove one frame, the dynamic quality vanishes immediately. The entire solar system is moving at a speed of 300 kilometers per second, as a geometrical point in the second orbit of the Milky Way galaxy. What would happen if we were to see this moving solar system from the side? Suppose the sun were to move in a straight line, although, of course, there is nothing really straight. Since the earth is rotating around the sun, while the sun moves, our planet is actually moving around it in a wave. Now, if we add the other planets, such as Jupiter and Mercury, we see that each of the planets has its own wavelength. When we see this more vividly, with the sun's motion forming the stem and root, we see how the solar system grows, just like a vegetable. In the ocean, there are many currents and waves; each of the planets is on a different wave, and these are all moving together.

Now we can see the unity of our solar system. We discover its particle unity. When we cut a cross-section, when we add this dimension of time, we see its wave unity. Light is just like this. Scientists have discovered both waves and particles, and they are wondering how to explain how both could exist at once.

Man is no different. We are yang, tiny, as a baby, and become more yin and expanded as we grow. When our growth is accomplished, a woman star comes, and we begin to create yang babies that become satellites around us. With more food and more expansion, more children come. In our old age, we begin to become more yang; our children become independent and form different waves. Finally our spouse dies; we become more yang, and finally die. All phenomena are like this; everything goes in waves. Since our senses see only one frame, we see particles. When we add the dimension of time, we see that everything is waving.

Our solar system, itself, is gradually becoming yanger. The outer, peripheral planets are coming closer to the sun. These waves, then, are becoming smaller and smaller. Eventually, after trillions of years, our system will decompose. Actually, long before this end is reached, our sun is constantly burning; planets are going into it, refueling it, new planets are being drawn into orbit, and it is radiating outward continuously. Our biological history began when this materialization was still going on, and spiritualization had already started. Humanity came out at the point when both activities had become even more intense. From this beginning to the present, more than three billion years have passed.

In the process of spiritualization or decomposition, heat, gas, electricity, radioactivity, radio waves, and many other phenomena are given off until the solar system finally disappears. When it was created, the infinite expansion gathered, with cosmic rays, radioactivity, and the rest, until matter appeared.

From this we can learn that everything is expansion and contraction. If we look through the glass of time, we see that all things are waving. Everything is flowing like a river. In a river we see many spirals that appear for a few moments and then melt into streams. The primary force of the universe is the infinite expansion. In one galaxy, the Milky Way, there are small particles, which are waving, and on one of these small particles man is living, claiming that he is the greatest in the universe.

This is the world of the Kingdom of Heaven. The Kingdom of Heaven's law is nothing but up and down, up and down, or yin-yang, yin-yang. Darkness changes into brightness, brightness changes into darkness, space changes into matter, matter changes into space, and everything is waving. This is the primary figure of the Kingdom of Heaven, and the primary figure of God itself. The law of God, or the law of the infinite universe, is very simple: everything waves. When you become a success, be cautious. When a civilization becomes grand, it will decline. When you are pretty, you may easily become ugly. When you become very clever, inevitably you will become a fool. This back and front is eternal law. There is nothing else but this infinitely moving stream.

In the Orient, in China, and India, there is no concept similar to the Western meaning of God, especially in the Far East. There is a Japanese word, "Kami," which is often translated as "God," but the meaning is actually quite different. The Chinese pronunciation is "Shin." The same word (but not the same character) is also used to mean "the top of the head," everything that is up, and "chewing." Here is how it originated. The first character is a table with something on it; it means "manifestation." The second character came from a picture of the sun; a line going through it indicates movement. Together, they mean extension, or expansion. The Oriental meaning of God, then, is "manifestation and expansion." This endless stream, expanding, yet manifesting, they called "God."

Perhaps you have heard of the Japanese "religion," Shinto. This word was actually a later Chinese pronunciation of an earlier Japanese word, "Kannagara no Michi," which is based on the words for "God," "stream," and "order of the universe." This is the original meaning of Shintoism. Instead of a God who punishes or makes laws, they had the order of the universe which they applied very practically to various aspects of the way of life. Daily manners were a part of Shintoism; respect for others, love of elders, respect for food, chewing well, making love, even making war, everything was one of the aspects of Shintoism. Everything was designed to follow this waving character of the order of the universe.

They loved and respected nature. If you went to the top of a hill, you would see a small shrine, honoring the hill. It would be a very humble shrine, perhaps built by some boy. Passing by a stream, you would see a small shrine. A great tree might have its own shrine. Stepping into the house you would find a miniature shrine in the living room. In the bedroom you would find another tiny shrine. They put shrines everywhere, and everywhere they thought of this manifestation of the infinite expansion; they saw the order of the universe in everything.

They were living with spirit, with this invisible order, so

they didn't care much about their physical life. They enjoyed this life, but if it were necessary to abandon it, fine! For justice, righteousness, or for honor and virtue, they gave it up. They evaluated degrees of justice. To keep my body, this is justice; to keep my friends, this is greater justice. For the greater justice they sacrificed the smaller justice. Kamikaze attacks, or harikiri, then, were carried out without any feeling of contradiction. They would gladly give up material wealth, honors, social position, and their lives for the sake of friendship and love.

You may say that this mentality is primitive. Yes, it is primitive. Yet, they were always thinking of this infinite expansion. They could not express it in words, as we are doing, but they felt it in their daily lives. Out of this they developed flower arranging (to make a miniature of the beauty of this stream of infinite expansion), the tea ceremony, graceful manners in serving meals, wonderful cooking, and many other traditions. Women, especially, were considered representatives of Kannagara no Michi, the way of the stream of infinity. It was because of this that a woman's education was strict. She was trained to be a good cook, a gracious, understanding, sympathizing person.

Now, of course, this intuitive comprehension of infinite order has disappeared, or is disappearing very rapidly. Traditionally, without being taught, they were feeling this until a few hundred years ago. Even the farmers felt it. Now, those who feel it in their daily lives are fewer and fewer. More and more, because of the changes in their eating habits, their senses are becoming sharp. As a result, they, too, see a fixed solar system, a frozen world, fixed momentarily and industrially. They are competing with each other, as we do in this country, to gain more material wealth and power. Because of this, modernization is going on very rapidly. Their strong constitutions, produced by centuries of good eating, have given them enormous vitality. More thatn a hundred million live on an island the size of California; they are now first in the world in ship building, second in consumption of automobiles and televisions, third in steel production, and so forth. This strong vitality is rooted in their traditional way of eating, although they are now becoming sick and degenerating very quickly, completely forgetting about their way of life.

Traditional Japan is ending. There is no more Japan, no more understanding of the waving stream of God. They have settled for a modern, civilized life. The customs and traditions that remain are nothing but relics of an understanding of the unity of life and death. We call the visible, materialized side, life; the invisible, death. It is something like sitting in the kitchen and seeing everyone arrive to eat. The dishes come out, the room is full of laughter, and good smells are in the air. If we return at night, everything has vanished. The dishes are washed and put away, the food is gone, and no one is in sight. Then, the next day, everyone reappears again. The dishes, the people, come and then disappear like phantoms, repeatedly. The same cycle goes on in our world. People come, then disappear; come, disappear.

Civilizations are no different; they rise, and then vanish. New ones come, and then vanish. Galaxies are born, then fade away. If we could watch one portion of space for trillions of years, we could see them dissolve into darkness, and then, from the darkness, see a new galaxy formed. It would shine for a while, and disappear. Soon another would come, life and death, brightness and darkness, are always alternating. Continents and oceans are changing in a cycle of millions of years. When winter comes, the flowers die; then, in spring they reappear. They are different, but very similar to the ones before. Life and death are something like this.

Suppose we are writing a sentence on a piece of paper. As we place a period, we are called to the telephone. The sentence has stopped. This is death. Ten minutes later, we come back and start a new sentence; this is life.

Life is something we can grasp by our senses. Death, darkness, is also moving, and just as light moves faster and reaches infinite speed, life becomes faster as it approaches infinity and becomes death. Without death, there could be nothing newly born, no resurrection or rebirth. What we call life is nothing but a phantom which we can catch with our senses. Perhaps our life is a dream, and death itself is real life. Fifty years from now, how many of us will be here? Seventy years later, we will have gone somewhere. No one will have remained on this earth as man or woman. New people will have come, and they will be arguing: "sugar is bad," or "brown rice is good," just like before. This order is continuously going on, eternally.

This great stream of infinity is cycling in a huge dimension of time. We call this one point the present; the past and the future are also cycling. Past becomes future, and future becomes past. The past equals future, and the future equals past. In the infinite scale—not in your lifetime, or in human history, but in infinity—past and future are the same. One changes into the other, and, in this infinite scale, there is alternation, creating similar types of things, again and again. A person very much like you, with your mentality, with your arrogance, foolishness, splendor, your handsomeness or beauty, may come out millions and millions of years from now, somewhere. He or she may even be speaking the same kind of language.

At this moment, there are millions of planets in this one universe with conditions similar to our earth's, and there is a great probability that human beings are living on many of them. They may have civilization like ours, or they may be more advanced or less developed; at any rate, they are our brothers and sisters, and they may be worrying about cancer, or the increase in their divorce rate, or enjoying ice cream.

Our consciousness is nothing but a camera that catches an image of this infinite stream. If our camera is of poor quality, our dream becomes very clouded. If it is working precisely like it should, we can see a very clear picture. We can freely make any kind of image of this infinite universe.

Our real dream is the endless stream. The waving, alternating, up and down movements are our desire. Our will is the same as this primary force of the infinite expansion. A strong will means a strong nervous system and brain, for these are the instruments that catch this stream and translate it into action. A strong will means good physical quality. You cannot interpret and perform this infinite universe's will if you are weak and sick from poor eating. If you want to make your will strong, it is very simple: just eat well, live an active life, and make your whole body clean.

Everyone is a replica of this wonderful universe we are living in. These expanding and contracting waves, forming matter and again dissolving, are the essence of our life and our body. Our nerves, for instance, are made of alternating strings and nodes. The lymphatic system is the same: fiber, node, fiber, node. Our bloodstream differentiates, branches outward, forms organs, and returns. Everything goes like this; stream, matter, stream, matter. Our life, our body, our society, our civilization, our history, our earth, our solar system, our Milky Way galaxy, everything goes in this order. This order is immortal; this order, you may say, is God's law, and nothing else.

Constant change is so interesting: success changes into failure, front changes into back, darkness changes into light. Everything is rise and fall, rise and fall. God's law is very simple. It has no concept of sin, or good and bad, but only front and back, up and down, and continuous change.

You can change yourself into anything you want. We, too, are both tiny, finite, geometric points or particles, and the waves of this infinite ocean. If you feel any unhappiness, you are limited. You have made yourself sick, and you have only to eat well to rediscover that everything in this universe is wonderful and happy.

11
Winter Vegetables

When winter came, traditional people continued to eat cereal grains and vegetables, which can easily be stored in the cold, as their main food. They also devised many interesting ways to keep vegetables without using chemicals or preservatives. Their methods adapted the summer produce into good food for winter time. Since cold weather is yin, they yangized their vegetables with salt, pressure, time, and dehydration.

The white radish, or diakon, which is harvested mainly in

autumn, was washed in cold water and laid in the autumn sunshine. Each night the radishes were covered, to protect them from the dew; every morning they were exposed to the sun again, until they finally became dehydrated. Within a week or so, these juicy, yin vegetables had become shrunken and hard. Then they were packed into barrels, with alternating layers of rice bran and plenty of salt. A wooden cover, which fit inside the barrel, was topped with a large, heavy stone. Finally, a dust cover was tied on, and the barrels were stored for at least six months and often for several years. The dates were recorded on the side, and the oldest ones were eaten first.

The finished product became brown from the rice bran, was somewhat flat, and very salty. Small pieces were sliced off and served with the main food. Although white radishes are originally yin, this process makes them more yang than animal food. A few slices, then, are usually enough. Not only radishes, but many other vegetables, can be kept in this manner. This process was invented by a Zen monk, Takuan, and has traditionally been named after him. A slice of pickle is simply called "Takuan." Carrots, burdock roots, and other vegetables, which are hard to begin with, need not be dried first, but can be put directly into the barrel.

For leafy vegetables, another technique is used. If we were to dry them, they would become yellowish and brown, and very distasteful. Since they are juicy, pressure would make them flood the barrel with water. A quicker method is employed, one which keeps them well for a few months, for use over one winter only. Chopped leafy vegetables and scallions, together with other vegetables, are placed in a barrel with sea salt or miso (a paste made from aged soybeans, sea salt, and wheat or barley), and picked out with long chopsticks when required. In this way, they become very yang and very delicious. You can try this method yourself, beginning to use the vegetables after only a few weeks. (As with all pickles, rinse quickly under cold water to remove any excess salt--ed.)

In these ways, ancient people stored vegetables. Other methods, such as simple drying or smoking (for fish), were also employed, but the combination of salt, pressure, time, and dryness was basic. Today, with quick transportation, everyone eats products from the southern climates when the ground is covered by snow, and the results are often a loss of adaptation to one's climate. These old methods are the best ways to enjoy vegetables throughout the winter while maintaining good health.

Umeboshi

Another food that people in the Orient traditionally processed in their homes is the umeboshi, or pickled plum. The tree from which it comes is generally yang. It grows horizontally (as compared to bamboo, for instance, which is very yin, shooting straight up). The flower appears in February, when the weather is cold (well before the April cherry blossoms). The fruit is produced directly from the flower, thousands on each tree. This yang tree produces a very yin, sour fruit, inedible and even dangerous.

The fruit is gathered in the early summer and spread by the thousands on the roofs of houses, on paper, wooden boards, or most preferably, rice straw mats. During the day, the plums become dehydrated by sunshine, and then at night they absorb dew and expand. As the days go by, the plums gradually become yang. Within a week or ten days they are ready to be placed in large earthenware jars, or more recently, in glass or wooden containers. They are still very yin, so they are alternated with layers of sea salt. Shiso leaves gives the plums a delightful taste and an appetizing reddish color. This purple grass is very yin, however, so it is used very sparingly. The jars are sealed with heavy lids that are weighed down by large stones.

In spite of the dehydration, the plums are still fairly moist when they are packed away. This excess liquid is removed by the salt and pressure, drawn off, and saved for various uses. It is especially delicious in salads and as a general vinegar substitute, and helps whenever a sour taste is required. Traditionally, it was used as a folk medicine for children's stomach pains and intestinal troubles.

The plums are usually aged for three or four years before being eaten. Oriental people considered them very helpful in regulating the digestive system, and took a little every day or one a week. Since the umeboshi is a combination of great yin and great yang, in harmonious balance, it was used to neutralize both acid and alkaline excesses in food. A case of diarrhea called for a salted plum, and one would be taken in bancha tea for indigestion. When traveling, they would make rice balls and place pieces of umeboshi in the center, which helped to protect them from impure local water and, by retarding the growth of bacteria, helped to keep the rice fresh much longer.

The umeboshi was a staple in almost every home for centuries. Today, with the advent of commercial processing, it has undergone great changes. Artificial chemical dyes are used as coloring agents instead of shiso leaves, and great heat is used to prepare them quickly in place of the slow, sure, traditional methods of aging. Sugar is often substituted for salt, and monosodium glutamate is added for flavor. Most families made their own umeboshi in the old days; even people in cities would buy fresh plums from the farmers and pickle them yearly. Today, even the farmers buy the inexpensive, commercialized, and greatly inferior umeboshi. Fortunately, a few families have preserved the traditional way of preparing salted plums, and we can purchase and enjoy these today in the United States.

12
Oriental Medicine

Many people have become interested in Oriental medicine recently. In Europe, there are several thousand doctors who are already practicing techniques imported from the East; numerous introductory publications are available. Since Europe often precedes the United States in new artistic, literary, philosophical, and professional interests, it is quite possible that this ancient outlook may soon spread to our country.

There is a basic difference in emphasis between all Eastern and Western medicines. In general, Western medicine concentrates on symptoms, while Eastern medicine treats each person as a whole. Of course, a Western doctor will always emphasize the importance of a regular checkup, and urge preventative measures, but the bulk of his efforts will be directed toward the diagnosis and elimination of symptoms. The Oriental physician, on the other hand, practically ignores symptoms, treating them as a side effect of a basic imbalance in the way of life. By seeing everything, he discovers what is wrong and directs his attention to the most fundamental problem. He may change his patient's food, his environment (food in a larger sense), or his view of life (the greatest food). Since he does not specialize, he can practice very widely, combining philosophy, theology, psychology, anatomy, and cosmology. Accordingly, he does not expect quick results.

Here are the qualifications of an Eastern medical man:

1. He must be a man of philosophy who knows life; that is, he knows that everything is changing.
2. He must cure his own sickness. Since he is free, he can become sick; but when he does, he must cure himself.
3. He should be a man of wisdom to know how to change mentality.
4. He must be a real man, or he cannot change other people.

His domain, then, is not limited to the treatment of sickness. He can apply his wisdom to everything, establishing harmony in the family and peace in the entire world. It is actually inaccurate, then, to call him a "physician." He cannot be labeled, typed, or titled with a degree. No classification fits him.

Naturally, for such a person, there is no need to use instruments, X rays, or needles. He is a very ordinary person, without need of a big office, or glass cases of implements. He does not deal in mysteries or miracles, for he wants to show a very simple way that everyone can follow. Even if he could heal miraculously, he will not use his abilities. Accordingly, he does not want to be called "master," "teacher," or "doctor."

When everyone else becomes sad, he becomes sad; when everyone else becomes happy, he becomes happy. He is the last to become happy, and he is very humble and moderate, because he knows the world is ephemeral and vanishing away. He does not make excuses to attackers, because he knows that they are sick and he is sad because his ability is not enough to make them happy. He appears to have unlimited patience, but actually has no concept of patience at all. Without sentimentality or any notion that he is saving others, he is enjoying his life to the utmost.

13
Evaluating Your Constitution

The spirals on the top of our head are a sign of our origin, and a good indication of our original constitution. A strong angle shows understanding; if it is toward the right, you may tend to be more active and aggressive in your outlook, even a little self-willed at times.

There are spirals everywhere in our body. Hold your thumbs together and look at your hands in the mirror. Do you see how the lines unite to circle inward from the fingers and down into the palm? A line that cuts straight downward and across the palm traditionally denotes success, a strong centripetality cutting directly from infinity toward a strong constitution. Our arms and legs are also spirals, developing outward from our body.

Another sign of original constitution is the angle formed by our eyes and our mouth. A broad, open triangle denotes a yin constitution, while a tight face with narrow eyes is likely to be more yang. Everything changes into its opposite eventually, so an originally yang person may have been attracted to plenty of yin food, such as fluids, sugar, and fruits, while growing, and become yin. This multi-dimensional vision is necessary, for yin always contains yang and vice-versa. Understanding of yin and yang cannot be gained by analytical methods; our intuition must be rediscovered and re-educated.

We can observe two kinds of yin facial structures: One is long and vertical, the other swollen horizontally. You may have seen the first face in many statues of Buddha and Japanese woodblock prints. The shape often resembles a grain of rice. Can you discover how they were formed? Both began with originally yang constitutions, and were attracted to yin foods. The first person, however, took yin from the beginning, while the second was fed more yang until around the age of ten. Since the face had reached its maximum vertical expansion, it began to balance the years of contraction by rapid horizontal growth.

We can divide everything into these two opposite, yet complementary, sides to answer the question of life. The nerve receptors for coldness are round (yang) in order to attract the yin cold. They operate by contracting (yang) and pressing to the cold. The nerves for detecting heat are very yin and diffuse, expanding and intermingling to stimulate our perceptions of warmth.

Ultimately, we can "make the two one," as Jesus said, uniting yin and yang to detect the real world lying behind them. Our taste buds, for instance, can determine both yin and yang tastes because they have an in-between structure, combining both characteristics. Everything has yin and yang, and we can sense infinity everywhere if our taste is keen enough. Yin and yang is nothing but the law of change, the comprehension of infinite motion. We offer these studies of yin and yang to encourage our friends to find the greatest dream, one that will never end.

Ears That Hear Infinity

Did you ever notice that most older people have long ears, with full, detached lobes? The ears of most younger people are generally higher on the head, smaller, and usually have small earlobes or none at all. Confirm this for yourself the next time you are in a crowd. You will be so surprised by the striking difference between the generations. What does it mean?

According to Eastern physiognomy, our ears are indicators of our original physical constitution. Ideally, they should cover the area from eye to mouth level. A person with ears like this can understand many people, appreciating life to the utmost. He can, literally, "hear infinity." Notice the ears on pictures and statues of Oriental Buddhas and saints. They are unusually long and well developed.

Let us imagine that the ears should continue to become shorter and higher on the head; finally, they would become like those of an animal. This is the biological direction toward which humanity is moving.

Our original constitution is determined by the food our mother eats while she is carrying us in her womb. Biologically speaking, this is the longest period of our life; here, we recapitulate evolution, developing three billion times from a single cell. The quality of our growth is the most important factor for determining all that follows.

The ear indicates the totality of this period of pregnancy. Grains and vegetable quality food produce long lobes; excessive amounts of animal food make them rise higher on the head and become smaller. Over the past fifty years, the consumption of grains in our country has fallen from the status of a main food to less than ten percent, while animal food has risen from ten to almost fifty percent. The amounts consumed have been reversed, and the results can be seen by observing the biological constitution of today's children.

A poor or a spoiled constitution can be overcome by following the way of eating. Everything changes, and if you know the order of the universe you can change unhappiness into happiness, defects into assets, enemies into friends. The first step is to return to grains and vegetables as the principal daily food. When an individual does this, his life changes toward freedom; when humanity does this, a new world can begin.

14
Ki

In the Orient, the concept of Ki, or life energy, was well understood, appreciated, and practically applied. Techniques of acupuncture were developed to treat its flow throughout the body, the martial arts were designed to utilize it properly, and many phenomena were related to it through the spoken and written languages.

In Japanese, the ideogram for *Ki* is made of the words for energy, which is drawn as the vibrations of yin and yang; atmosphere, which signifies movement; and the ideogram for rice. Here are a few words using Ki:

Ten Ki: weather (Ki of heaven)
Ku Ki: air (Ki of emptiness)
Byo Ki: sickness (sick Ki)
Ki Chigai: madness (wrong Ki)
Yu Ki: courage (active Ki)
Ki Ga Tsuku: notice (Ki is attached or focused)
Ki Ga Kawaru: change mind (Ki changed)
Ki Ga Kiku: clever (Ki works sharply)
Ki Ga Noru: want to do (Ki rides)
Ki Ga Chisai: coward (Ki is small)
Ki Ga Shizumu: depressed (Ki sinks down)
Ki Ni Iru: come to like (Ki is accepted)
Ki O Tsukau: worry about (use Ki)
Jo Ki Suru: excitement (Ki goes up high)
Ki O Tobasu: frightened (Ki flies away)
Ki O Ushinau: fall down unconscious (Ki is lost)
Sho Ki: sound consciousness (right Ki)
Ki Hin: nobleness (Ki is good for three factors)
Uwa Ki: chasing girls (floating or wandering Ki)

Calories and Ki

According to the modern theory, energy for human activity depends upon calories contained in our daily food that are supplied mainly by various forms of sugar and starch. In this commonly accepted way of thinking, there is an increasing tendency to believe that increased consumption of caloric sources contributes positively to more energetic activity. As a result, as the generations pass, the recommended caloric consumption for an individual increases. At the present time, the prescribed amount of calories in the United States generally averages about 2000 or more, depending on age, sex, condition, and activity level.

However, energy for human activity does not depend exclusively upon the amount of calories taken in. As we experience daily, our human life has two aspects—physical and mental. It is undeniable that our physical activity owes much to the calories we consume and burn within our body; but our daily experiences show us that our mental activity often decreases with more caloric consumption, and that often we think much more clearly when we decrease our intake of food. Jesus, Buddha, and many others have realized great spiritual attainment after a period of fasting. It is a fact that, among many kinds of mental experiences, the most fundamental functions—that of the intuitive judgment—do not require any calories in order to be active.

These antagonistic factors of human activity--our physical and mental functions—should be well coordinated. We need to find the means to balance them, in each individual, without emphasizing or preferring one over another. In order to solve this problem, we would like to offer the Oriental concept of Ki, which, throughout the ages, has been considered the most important faculty for the exercise of both physical and mental development. For the time being, we wish to translate this word, Ki—which represents invisible force working throughout the universe, including all beings—as electromagnetic force.

This invisible, and therefore immeasurable force, is working in all of our human activities and in all of the changing phenomena of our universe. We take this force into us as we need it, just as we take our daily food. We can characterize it as a yin factor, while food is yang by comparison, due to its visible and measurable nature.

Because these two are antagonistic and complementary, we need to find the proper quantity of food, as well as the proper quality, in order to draw this electromagnetic force and let it flow at maximum efficiency. Because quantity affects quality, the amount of food determines whether this force is more or less effectively absorbed and allowed to operate in our body. The energy for our human activity is thus made up of food, which exists in the form of visible matter (yang), plus electromagnetic force, or Ki, which takes the form of nonmaterial energy (yin). Present theories of nutrition and calories will become much more comprehensive when they come to include the invisible aspects of our human life, that is, our mental and spiritual functions. When this has come to pass, we shall understand why most ancient religions and philosophical teachings had principles of nutrition similar to the one we have outlined, and quite different from present theories, in order to achieve the highest human capacities and to develop our mental and physical functions as a whole.

15
Humanity's Traditional Food

Throughout history, grains have been humanity's principal food. Every great culture cultivated corn, rice, wheat, barley, oats, rye or buckwheat, and these plants were often worshipped as the sacred source of life.

"Rice and wheat are man's principal foods," according to a recent study made by the U. S. Department of Agriculture, which found that over half of the present world's supply of food energy comes from grains. Indeed, humanity cannot live without these unique products of the vegetable kingdom; more than 70 percent of our croplands are devoted to their production. Our ancestors called grains "the staff of life," and every year archeologists discover them in the most venerated areas of ancient cities. Our modern chemical analysis shows us why. They are complete, balanced, whole foods, containing abundant carbohydrates, proteins, fats, minerals and vitamins in excellent proportions. One hundred grams of brown rice, for example, contains 337 calories, 15.5 gm. water, 7.4 gm. protein, 2.3 gm. fat, 72.5 gm. carbohydrate, 10 gm. calcium, 3 mg. sodium, 300 mg. phosphorous, and 1.1 mg. iron. Brown rice is especially rich in the important B vitamins. Moreover, it has the quality of life, an aspect often overlooked by analytical studies.

The story of grains is the history of our human species. Whenever they have grown, civilization and culture have flourished; when they have been abandoned, humanity has become chaotic. A well-known country provides a good example. As it grew, it fed itself with grains, and its people were happy and active; later, however, as it ate less and less grains, it became sick. Mental illness and severe social unrest threatened to shake it apart at the foundations.

This is the story of modern America. Our ancestors built this country with strong bodies and clear judgment nourished by grains. They were cooking oatmeal, baking their own bread, preparing vegetables picked from their own gardens, and eating much smaller proportions of animal food than we have become accustomed to today. They were strong, and they knew the purpose of life intuitively.

Today, three out of five marriages end in divorce. Two out of five persons suffer from heart attacks, and one out of four from cancer. What will our country be like in another twenty years? It seems that America is now ending. According to the U. S. Department of Health, Education and Welfare, mental illness affects one out of ten. Sexual unhappiness is common. This is not the happy sort of life that our ancestors knew. Fifty years ago, our diet was over 50 percent grains and about 10 percent animal food; today these figures are reversed. Never has a country consumed so much animal food and so little grains. Even the small portion still consumed is refined and treated.

Why are grains so important to humanity?

The most basic answer lies in the story of evolution. Most of the accepted theories of evolution concentrate on heredity and environment, but overlook the most essential factor: the importance of food. Food is the means of evolution. By changing our food, we change ourselves.

When an animal moves to a warmer climate, for example, he begins to eat the vegetation around him, which is quite different from his normal fare. The new plants are more lush, juicy, and expanded, and they enable him to adapt to this new environment. He begins to change, and his offspring are correspondingly different. Over the generations a new species evolves, well suited to the warmer weather. The vegetable world, which adapts itself to changes in climate quickly and efficiently, automatically helps us to make a balance when we eat food which is grown in our own locale.

Humanity has changed food many times in the process of evolution. Grains were the last link in this chain, and they enabled humanity to develop thinking power, to stand upright, to become fully human. The last refinement came when we began to cook our food. Cooking gave us freedom from coldness and sudden changes in climate, so that we could live anywhere and do anything. This new kind of food also changed our physical constitution, making us more active and self-sufficient. Grains and vegetables, then, and the art of cooking, produced humanity. Together, they can give us the secret for a new future.

Our teeth give us a clue to what our daily food should be. Almost 80 percent of them are best suited for grinding grains. The front teeth, which comprise about 15 percent, are cutting teeth, excellent for eating vegetables. Between these two kinds of teeth lie the canine or tearing teeth, suitable for animal food. These are good proportions to observe in our daily diet.

The great religions taught the importance of eating grains. In the first chapter of Genesis, verse 29, God speaks to Adam: "Behold, I have given you every herb bearing seed, which is upon the face of all the earth, and every tree, in which is the fruit of a tree yielding seed: to you it shall be for meat." In the first chapter of the Book of Daniel, the king Nebuchadnezzar has the most talented youth of the land brought to his palace, and gives a command that they eat the meat and drink from his kitchen. At the end of three years, they were to be presented before the king. As we read in the Bible:

> But Daniel proposed in his heart that he would not defile himself with the portion of the king's meat, nor with the wine which he drank; therefore he requested of the prince of the eunuchs that he might not defile himself." (Daniel asked him,) "Prove our servants, I beseech thee ten days; and let them give us pulse (grain) to eat, and water to drink. Then let our countenance be looked upon before thee, and the countenance of the children that eat of the portion of the king's meat: and as thou seest, deal with thy servants.
>
> So he consented to them in this matter, and proved them ten days. And at the end of ten days their countenances appeared fairer and fatter in flesh than all the children which did eat the portion of the king's meat. Thus Melzar took away the portion of their meat, and the wine that they should drink; and gave them pulse. As for these four children, God gave them knowledge and skill in all learning and wisdom: and Daniel had understanding in all visions and dreams.
>
> Now at the end of the days that the king has said he should bring them in, then the prince of the eunuchs brought them in before Nebuchadnezzar. And the king communed with them; and among them all was found none like Daniel, Hananiah, Mishael, and Azariah (who had all been eating grains): therefore stood they before the king. And in all matters of wisdom and understanding that the king inquired of them, he found them ten times better than all the magicians and astrologers that were in all his realm.

Jesus said, "Give us this day our daily bread," and recent discoveries even seem to indicate that the importance of eating grains was a central aspect of his teaching, so commonsensical that it has been forgotten. Buddhism, Taoism, Hinduism, Confucianism, Judaism, Christianity, and other great religions all come from peoples who were eating grains from either knowledge or tradition, and all of them taught food disciplines that center around grains.

If we were to return to grains as our principal food, we could easily solve the "population explosion." A statement published by the Wheat Flour Institute and reviewed by the American Medical Association explains why. "Because of the nourishment offered by abundant wheat, it is our most economical food. Arable land planted with wheat will provide food for more people than the same land used for producing non-cereal food, like meat, milk or poultry. To say it another way, it has been estimated that about eight pounds of feed grain are required to produce one pound of meat. Eight pounds of wheat offer far greater quantities of many needed nutrients than the one pound of meat." With grains, we could feed ten times the world's population easily.

When we eat grains, we are simply using our common sense. "Wa," the Japanese word for "peace," is made of the words for "mouth" and "rice." There are thousands of people throughout the world today who have found through their own personal experience that eating grains makes them happy and peaceful. To create a new world—this, above everything, is the best reason for us to return to humanity's traditional food.

16
Diet and Nutrition

There are many recent studies, well-documented with case histories, linking sugar with mental illness, criminality, and physical degeneration. The almost inescapable conclusion one reaches after examining these documents is that the enormous increase in the consumption of sugar in our civilization is an important contributor to the world crisis we are facing today.

Why, then, does sugar seem so good? Should we suppress

our desire for sweetness?

Not at all. Sugar is essential to our life. Whenever we act, our cells decompose sugar and release energy. This simple chemical action is the center of our entire metabolism. However, there are many kinds of sugars, such as glucose, fructose, maltose, lactose, dextrose, and sucrose, and each of them has a different effect. The key to solving the enigma of sugar depends on the distinction of quality.

There are three main types of sugar:

1. simple sugars (monosaccharides)
2. double sugars (disaccharides)
3. complex sugars (polysaccharides)

The sugar in fruits and honey is a monosaccharide; that in sugar cane and milk is a disaccharide; and that in grains and beans is a polysaccharide. In the process of digestion, the more complex sugars are broken down into double sugars in the mouth and then into simple sugars in the intestines before finally being changed into energy. If we take a shortcut in this process by eating simple sugars, natural functions are disrupted and metabolic and organic disharmony results.

Grain sugar, for example, is decomposed by saliva, further broken down in the stomach and finally digested in the duodenum by the action of juices from the liver, gallbladder, and intestines. A simple sugar, on the other hand, does not need to be chewed; it passes immediately to the stomach, which stops its digestive actions immediately. This "sugar reaction" can be caused by milk, fruit, honey, or as little as one quarter of a teaspoon of sugar. These strong alkaloids (yang) attract the acid (yin) gastric juices of the stomach and disturb the pH factor, producing over-acidity. If this continues, the acids begin to work on the walls of the digestive tract and ulcers begin to form.

The simple sugars pass through the stomach, reach the intestines, and enter the bloodstream at once. The complex sugars are broken down more slowly and are gradually absorbed into the blood. In both cases, the end result is a release of water and energy:

$$C_6H_{12}O_6 + 6O_2 = 6H_2O + \text{energy}$$

These different rates of digestion have very different side effects. The metabolism of grain sugars may be compared to a fire that is evenly fed and carefully tended, resulting in a warm, steady bed of coals with an even, dancing flame. Now suppose we were to pour a can of gasoline onto this fire. What would happen? A quick glaring flame would result, which would burn down quickly, leaving the room full of smoke and the fireplace charred with soot. That is what happens when we eat refined sugar. An uneven and excessively alkaloid reaction is followed by an acid condition that creates tiredness.

So essential is balance to our body that it has many ways to provide against such sudden shocks. Minerals, such as sodium (from salt), potassium and magnesium (from vegetables), and calcium (from the bones) are mobilized and used in a chemical reaction, producing neutral acids that return the pH factor of the blood to a more normal state.

If sugar is taken every day, producing a continuously over-acid condition, more and more minerals are required from deep within the body. Finally, in order to protect the blood, so much calcium is taken from the bones and teeth, that decay and general weakening starts.

Excess sugar eventually affects every organ in the body. First, it is stored in the liver in the form of glycogen. Since the liver's capacity is limited to an optimum 50 grams, a daily intake above the required amount soon makes it expand like a balloon. When the maximum is reached, the excess glycogen is returned to the blood in the form of fatty acids. These are then taken to every part of the body and stored in the most inactive areas, such as the belly, the buttocks, and thighs.

After being stored in these comparatively harmless places, the fatty acids begin to be distributed among the active organs. These yang organs, such as the heart and kidney, begin to slow down and become ineffective, and finally their tissues start to degenerate and change into fat. The whole body is affected by their reduced ability and abnormal blood pressure soon begins.

Sugar cane is a tropical plant, and could be more suitably eaten (as food for pleasure) in a very warm climate. Our modern transportation methods violate this order of the universe, with the result that many people who live in the North have physical conditions suited for sunny climates. Refined sugar is especially deleterious, for it lacks the natural minerals that create a balance in the cane plant. When this refined product is introduced into our body, it must seek what it lacks and our stock of minerals becomes depleted.

Being a tropical plant, sugar tends to make us more yin to balance the yang climate in which it is grown. Our parasympathetic nervous system is affected, and the organs governed by it, such as the small brain, become inactive or even paralyzed. It invades the circulatory and lymphatic systems, which begin to become sugary instead of maintaining their normally salty condition. The quality of the red globules starts to change; they become weaker, and the creation of tissue becomes slower. White cells also weaken, so that our tolerating, immunizing power becomes more limited; we cannot respond properly to extreme attacks from without.

Excessive sugar intake also has a strong effect on the functions of the brain. The function of our judgment is to decide, in any situation, whether we proceed (go ahead) or control (stop). The key to this ability is glutamic acid, a vital compound found in many vegetables. When you taste sweetness in cooked carrots and onions, for example, you are detecting glutamic acid. This divides into two antagonistic-complementary compounds. One of them produces a "proceed" reaction, the other a "control" response. The B vitamins play a very important part in this change.

Grains are rich in B vitamins, and are very helpful in producing clear thinking. These vitamins are also manufactured by symbiotic bacteria living in the intestines. When we take plenty of sugar every day, these bacteria die, and our stock of the B vitamins becomes very low. Often we become sleepy, and if we take too much sugar, we lose our ability to calculate and remember.

Freckles are a sign of excess sugar being discharged from

the skin. Sugar (yin) is attracted to the heat (yang) of the sun. Most modern people become very dark if they expose themselves to the sun. Until very recently this was considered a sign of ill health in many cultures. Of course, if we have this excess in us, we feel better after it is reduced, but it might be better not to have so much in us to begin with. The Japanese word for "happy" and "healthy" means "white face."

According to the 1968 World Almanac, the average American is now consuming 97.9 pounds of sugar per year. This accounts for 6.5 percent of our total diet, and does not include the sugar found in processed foods. Grains, the traditional food of humanity, have reached a low of 9.5 percent of the total diet. It is no wonder that the modern world is facing a health crisis of unprecedented proportions.

Milk

Cow's milk is produced for calves, human milk for babies. Their compositions and effects are markedly different. Here is a brief comparison for consideration:

*Both were designed to be taken directly from the breast, without exposure to air. As soon as this happens, bacteria begin to form. Since we are compelled to allow cow's milk to become exposed, we must add preservatives to it, which changes its chemical structure and its effectiveness.

*The protein in human milk is mainly soluble lactal bumin, while that in the cow's milk is insoluble caseinogen. Human milk, being soluble, is readily digestible in the stomach, while cow's milk is not.

*The fat in human milk is a more finely emulsified type, with less fatty acids than cow's milk. These factors are important in securing flexibility and adaptability for our body.

*Human milk does not cause digestive sickness; cow's milk does, when taken in excess.

*Human milk transfers the agents of immunization which the mother carries in her blood to her baby.

*Human milk has more lactose than cow's milk.

*Human mothers produce colostrum, which comes out

from three to five days after birth, before the normal milk begins to flow. This includes various proteins and corpuscles that are believed to produce immunization in babies and protect them for several months by giving them resistance to infectious diseases.

*Each form of milk has a different pH reaction, which creates different forms of digestibility and different blood quality in the body.

Finally we can observe that milk is nature's perfect food for babies. No animal drinks it after he is weaned. Why, then, should we?

Proteins, Carbohydrates, and Fats

Proteins, carbohydrates, and fats are recognized as the essential building blocks for our body. Here are their main vegetable sources:

Carbohydrates	Proteins	Fats (oil)
grains	grains	grains
vegetables	beans	seeds

Grains and beans are especially rich sources of protein. In addition, their protein score is high. This is a measure to determine the quality of protein. There are various amino acids, ten of which are considered essential. When these predominate in a given protein, the score is counted high. The perfect score would be 100, which is non-existent. The protein score for brown rice is 72, which is very high.

Here are the percentages of protein in various vegetable and animal foods:

Vegetable Food	Protein	Animal Food	Protein
brown rice	7.5	beef	20.4
barley	9.6	pork	21.4
wheat	14.0	ham	22.7

buckwheat	11.7	chicken	21.0
sesame seeds	18.6	eggs	12.7
soybeans	34.1	milk	3.0
azuki beans	20.9	cheese	25.2
tamari soy sauce	6.0	fish	20.0
miso	12.6		

Not only do grains and beans have comparable amounts of protein, but the difference in quality is considerable. Vegetable quality protein is superior to animal quality protein, in many respects. When we eat animal food, we take hard, saturated fats along with protein. As a result, cholesterol begins to collect around the organs. Animal proteins create toxins in the digestive system, and our excrement begins to smell bad. A person who eats mainly vegetable protein and carbohydrates has no need for perfumes, disinfectants, and deodorants, which are nothing more than inventions of people who depend on animal food for a good portion of their diet.

Our metabolism is a plasmic process, a dynamically moving transmutation of carbohydrates into proteins, into energy or fats. Heavier elements, such as sodium, phosphorous, and iron, decompose into lighter elements such as carbon and hydrogen, which are then built into proteins. If we take animal proteins as our daily food, an environment is created in our intestines that is unhealthy for the intestinal bacteria that help us to make these transmutations. Since modern doctors have always examined subjects who were eating diets based on animal food, they have never had a chance to observe this process. In order to restore the body's natural abilities, certain soybean products, beans and fish are very helpful while making a transition to a carbohydrate-based diet.

The quality of every animal protein is different, and this uniqueness is imparted to us when we eat it. Fish, fowl, eggs and meat all produce different effects. The essential structure of the amines are retained when our blood cells are formed, and we tend to become like our food. The quality of protein in fish is far superior to that found in red meat.

Soybean Products and Azuki Beans

The soybean has been called the "vegetable cow" of the Orient. It is extremely high in good quality protein. Tamari is the traditional soy sauce, free of chemicals and preservatives, and miso is a paste made from soybeans and wheat or barley, used in making bouillon-like soups and many other delicious, energizing foods. Both of them are treated with sea salt and aged for several years to yangize the beans.

Other beans, especially azuki beans, chickpeas (garbanzo beans) and lentils, are also excellent sources of protein. Azuki beans are especially interesting. It was common knowledge in the ancient Orient that these small red beans were the best food for poor kidneys. They are the most yang bean and when properly cooked, are often voted the most delicious.

Fats

There are different qualities of fats, just as there are different qualities of protein. Saturated and unsaturated fats are very different in their effects on the body. Hard, saturated fats, found in animal food, are great contributors to hardened arteries. This kind of fat is very harmful, producing many undesirable effects.

It is a mistake, however, to conclude that all fats are to be avoided. Unsaturated, liquid fat, which is obtained from vegetables, is necessary for a smoothly functioning human body. Our nerve cells need vitamin E, or linoleic acid, which is one of the unsaturated fats. If you do not take a sufficient amount of vegetable quality fat, your thinking is likely to deteriorate. Without lipotine, found in unsaturated fats, the metabolism of the cells becomes sluggish. Lecithin, which coats each blood cell, is a protective fatty acid which is donated by these oils. If we are "properly oiled," all of our organic processes can become smoothly coordinated.

Recently, our food patterns have changed greatly. Much more saturated fats are being taken, resulting in an increase in stroke, heart attacks, and hardening of the arteries. Since animal products tend to decay in the intestines, strong chemicals are usually added to them after they are killed. In the process of digestion, the animal proteins are broken down into amino acids, which are then decomposed by intestinal bacteria into poisonous amines. A new species of bacteria begins to develop, one of which tends to create ulcerous conditions. High sugar intake contributes to this, and constipation and gas results. The ulcers allow blood capillaries to take proteins without decomposition, allergies begin to develop from abnormal blood conditions, and lecithin begins to melt away.

Finally, a septic condition arises throughout the bloodstream. The outcome of septicemia can be death, preceded by sicknesses and general weakness. The tongue is a good indicator of the condition of the intestines; if it is any color but pinkish, there is usually trouble. Cancer is a fortress to defend against this bad quality of blood; operations designed to remove it are fighting against a protective mechanism of the body. Those who have cancer, without exception, are found to have had intestinal trouble for many years.

Some Japanese scholars tested a group of people who were eating a diet high in animal food, and found that they had many toxic bacteria within their intestines. After changing to a diet of grains and vegetables, rich in unsaturated fats, with a small quantity of animal food, these bacteria decreased to less than one-half of their former amount within one month.

The best source of saturated fats is vegetable seeds. Grains, squash and sesame seeds are all recommendable. Many ways have been devised to extract the oil from seeds. Crushing machines were invented, but this left about twenty percent of the oil unused. Heat was then applied to melt the oil. Today, chemicals are employed to extract oils; this is the process used in supermarket varieties. None of these methods is entirely satisfactory. High temperatures destroy some of the good qualities of the unsaturated fats and chemicals are deleterious in themselves. The surest, best way is by grinding the seeds at low temperatures in your own mouth. Strong grinding is next best, and commercial methods are the least preferable. A suribachi, or Japanese grinder, is an excellent, though seemingly inefficient, technique.

In general, our modern theories of nutrition emphasize protein and de-emphasize fats and carbohydrates. This is a very recent concept in the history of humanity, current only in the past 150 years. Usually, carbohydrates have been our main food. As we have seen, however, sensitive determination of quality is most important in discussing these matters. Relativity has been applied in physics but not in nutrition and medical science.

Most of our modern theories are only necessary when we are taking large amounts of animal food. Most of these ideas originated in Germany, a country with a traditionally large consumption of animal food. The mechanism to determine proper diet was analytical; scientists examined the body, found that it was composed of protein and concluded that we must eat mainly protein. Then, having settled on animal food as the best source of protein, they were forced to seek stronger and stronger forms of yin to make balance: vitamin C, chemicals, medicines, and raw vegetables.

A good example of the way this can work occurred when British sailors contracted scurvy, and were cured with citrus fruits. They were working hard (yang), breathing salt air (yang) under a hot sun (yang), and their daily food was salted meat (double yang). Their only form of yin was their daily portion of grog. When they were given the extreme yin of the fresh citrus fruits, their condition became more balanced and the swollen legs and bleeding gums characteristic of scurvy disappeared. Since then, citrus fruits have been considered necessary for daily food.

Since our consumption of animal food has continued to rise, we have continued to discover stronger forms of yin, such as sugar, spices, ice cream, stronger chemicals, and vegetarian or fruitarian diets. Alcoholism and drug addiction are nothing more than an attempt to make balance for this excessive intake of animal food.

In conclusion, protein is certainly necessary, and is especially good when taken in vegetable form. Fats, too, are important when they are of the unsaturated, vegetable variety.

The importance of carbohydrates has been overlooked, but scientists are beginning to rediscover this traditional food. A balanced measure of all of these essential elements is amply provided in a diet based on grains and vegetables.

17
Blood Quality

The quality of our blood is the basis of all of our happiness and unhappiness. If our blood is good, we can create and enjoy life without disease and react in any situation without recourse to doctrines or disciplines. If it is bad, our world is limited, and our direction is toward physical and mental sickness.

Each tiny red blood cell has a nucleus of iron. As you know, iron is used to make compass needles because it is very sensitive to electric currents and easily magnetized. When these cells are in good condition, they automatically point us toward our direction, enabling us to enjoy the utmost flexibility and to adapt to any environment or change of circumstances, while going toward our greatest goal.

The only fundamental way to maintain our blood quality is through good eating, for our blood cells are produced directly from what we absorb in our small intestines. When we see our daily food, we know what we will become within twenty-four hours.

The center of our physical gravity is situated two fingers below our navel, where our small intestines lie. If we stretch our arms above our head, this point will lie halfway between our fingers and our feet. In many Oriental teachings this spot, variously referred to as the "Tanden," or "Hara," was emphasized.

Most modern authorities believe that blood is manufactured in the bone marrow, though some disagree and give evidence that it comes from other places. Actually, according to the hypothesis we discuss below they are all right, and all wrong.

Here is how this confusion originated. The tests which have been made to determine the location of red blood cell manufacture have used subjects who have been fasting for some time. When we fast, our blood, unable to obtain a fresh supply of globules from food, begin to draw on the supply which has been stored everywhere in the body. Thus, if we look at the bone marrow or the organs of a fasting subject, there is a good chance that we will see blood cells coming out.

Recently, two Japanese doctors, Chisima and Morishita, examined subjects that had not been fasting and discovered that the red blood cells go to the organs and change directly into organ tissue. The usual medical theory is that growth in cells takes place by cellular division, one liver cell changed into two. The reason for this theory is that, again, experiments have always been carried on under abnormal conditions, in test tubes, with special environments, which produce an unusual reaction.

According to this hypothesis, food, then, changes into blood and blood changes into organs, which in turn break down food and clean the blood. If the blood is clean and healthy it can travel to every part of the body and remove waste products and oxygenate tissues quickly and speedily. If we are truly healthy, we will have energy and endurance, and need little sleep. The organ that consumes the most blood is the brain; if it is well cleansed and vivified, we can think, adapt and discover life anew at every moment.

Our bloodstream is our river of life. For most of us, however, it is a somewhat septic river, a little polluted and clogged. Our red globules are yinnized from sugar, chemicals, and drugs—making them, and us, confused and uncertain of our direction.

Let us follow this journey of transformation from food to our cells. The first step is digestion which actually begins in our pressure cooker or skillet when we cook our food. Lower animals, such as the snake, often bolt their food while more advanced animals begin to chew. Chewing makes digestion much easier, thinking clearer and advances evolution in the direction of happiness. (An old Japanese word for "chewing" is "God work.") We even go a step further and begin to digest food while it is still outside of us. The discovery of cooking enabled humanity to develop sensitive abilities of feeling and thinking.

Saliva is alkaloid (yang), and the principal factor in the digestion of carbohydrates. Proteins are digested mainly in the stomach and fats in the intestines. Since grains are digested well in the mouth, it is important to chew them thoroughly. Having been yangized through chewing and the action of the saliva, they can travel downward toward the stomach. Being yang, they attract stomach acids (yin), which decompose them further. It is recommended to begin a meal with the most yang food and progress toward the most yin; otherwise, these juices cannot come out and digestion will not be so smooth.

Finally, the food reaches the small intestines in the form of a homogeneous liquid that is ready to be absorbed into the bloodstream. The small intestine is a jungle, a forest of hair, with millions of bacteria and viruses furthering transmutation by eating food, changing its quality with their enzymes and discharging it. Animal foods, strong acids such as sugar and fruits, medicines, drugs and chemicalized foods kill these bacteria and cause indigestion. Miso, which is rich in healthy bacteria, is very helpful in promoting and rebuilding the intestine's transmuting abilities.

Molecules of this jellified food become attached to the ends of these hairs, or villi, and are absorbed by the small intestine. According to the hypothesis presented above, as these molecules move up the villi, they form links in chains of nuclei which finally reach the blood capillaries, where they become blood cells. First they become white blood cells; later, the white blood cells can change into red blood cells.

The first white cells are called primary white cells. It is possible for a red cell to change into a white cell again, in which case a secondary white cell is formed. This process is continually going on according to our food intake. White blood cells are yin; red blood cells are yang. If we take sugar, red cells change into white cells; if we eat salt, white cells change into red cells. Leukemia, a condition characterized by too many white blood cells is caused by sugar and other yin foods, while scurvy, an excess of red blood cells, is a sign of excess yang.

We can see that our body is a transitory stage between food and energy, a delicate transmuting machine, in which chlorophyll, the essence of plant life, is changed into hemoglobin, the essence of animal life. This occurs through the transmutation of magnesium into iron.

Magnesium (Chlorophyll) → Iron (Hemoglobin)
Vegetable World — Animal World

Magnesium (Mg) collects lighter elements around itself, such as oxygen, hydrogen and nitrogen and forms chlorophyll. Iron, by a similar process, becomes the nucleus for hemoglobin. Magnesium can change directly into hemoglobin by the addition of oxygen; simply by breathing, we can make our tissues directly from vegetable food. Here is how this happens. Since it is difficult for oxygen to combine with magnesium, the latter is broken down into two carbons.

$$ {}^{12}_{24}Mg \rightarrow {}^{6}_{12}C + {}^{6}_{12}C $$

Carbon is very yang inside, attracting many elements to itself and has an adaptable exterior, allowing these elements to join. It is easy to see why carbon is the most essential building block for living compounds. It combines with oxygen and forms iron.

$$ 2\,O^{8}_{20} + 2\,C^{6}_{12} \rightarrow Fe^{26}_{56} $$

Finally the hemoglobin goes to each part of the body and changes into the sort of tissue needed, whether it be bone, fat, nerve, or organ tissue. If the hemoglobin is of good quality, the organ can become healthy. Our happiness, then, depends on nothing more complicated than the quality of our blood, which is a transmutation of our daily food.

18
What is Love?

Everyone knows what love is, but who can explain it? We need a simple, practical explanation that everyone can understand. Too often we give our lives to ideas that cannot be explained practically. If we cannot express our greatest dreams in language that is simple and direct, we run the risk of becoming slaves to empty concepts and relative thinking.

This is especially true of the strongest, most powerful men, those who have succeeded on the battlefield of the world, only to lose everything to a pretty smile. "Love conquers all," we say; we might add, "weakness conquers strength." This seems to work especially well against those who try to avoid it. In this world, power is respected very much, and most people seek it without a second thought. They cultivate physical strength, spend the majority of their days as employees to earn money, train themselves to have opinions to gain authority, and study to achieve power in art, knowledge, and techniques.

All of these things are of the world of relativity. Since this is the world we live in, most seek these things for their lives. In this yang world of competition, men fight for power more than women do, spending their days to achieve the power they desire. And yet, even if a man achieves the ultimate in his endeavors, he surrenders to woman, for she is yin. Without seeking physical power, money, authority, or art, she conquers all. The stronger, more energetic, more powerful a man is, the more he is attracted to woman. This is the paradoxical construction of the relative world.

The Constitution of the Sexes

Men and women are constructed differently; they are antagonistic, complementary opposites. The distinction seems obvious, but in the modern world, it is often misunderstood. For instance, if the difference between men and women were appreciated, it is doubtful that coeducation would exist. In traditional societies, these differences were recognized, and boys and girls were educated differently. There is nothing symmetrical in this universe. Since we have failed to recognize this, men and women are given similar educations, with the result that they are becoming more alike and the attraction between them is growing less.

We should always look behind the appearance of things to see their inner structure; this is the key to true understanding. For instance, man's interior is actually yin; thus he seeks more yang food and becomes yang. Each factor always contains its opposite, every front has a back. Let us study the construction of man and woman with this in mind.

Woman, yin, produces an egg, which is yang—round and solid. Man, being yang, produces a yin reproductive cell, the sperm. Each of these, in turn, have two general classifications: there are yin and yang eggs, yin and yang sperm. The condition of the reproductive cell is primarily a result of the physical condition of the individual who produces it. Our modern geneticists have overlooked this completely in their search for hereditary patterns. Changes of season and food produce quite different eggs and sperm; summer, for instance, and drugs, tend to make them yin. The combination of these factors decides the sex and general development of the child during its early growth in the womb. If the man is relatively more yin, a son will be produced. In theory, then, the sex of a child can be decided by his parents. To have a son, a mother needs to make herself more yang during the six months prior to conception.

Conception determines the original bent of the child, but the most important factor in its development is still to come. The nourishment that its mother takes while it is in the womb is all-important, for during this time, it grows three billion times its original weight, retracing the evolutionary development of the human species. The fetus, however, chooses the food it needs from what its mother presents to it; it is in this way that sexual differences develop. The yang male cell attracts yin food, and develops a yin body with the sexual organs on the outside. The more yin female cell attracts more yang food, and develops a more yang structure with the sexual organs inside the body. If the mother eats good quality food, the child can choose good food to nourish itself with; if the mother eats poorly, the child will develop accordingly.

At birth, then, the boy is yin, the girl yang. As they grow, the boy seeks yang food and becomes masculine; the girl seeks yin and becomes feminine. (In our modern civilization, of course, this eating pattern is widely violated.) The inner structure of the sexes is the opposite of their appearance. Men have more hair, which is yin, because they are originally yin; thus, the yin they take becomes excess. A smooth-skinned person has a yang constitution. Although a man is strong and independent, he is attracted to the worlds of spirituality and passivity. Since a woman is yin, she can live longer than most men; she is more receptive and physically weaker, but she can be extremely determined and possess great inner strength. It takes her longer to become yang as she grows older, hence her greater longevity.

Men and women are each attracted to their opposite, both in the relative and absolute worlds. They should seek the greatest antagonist they are capable of in order to realize their greatest dream. Man, who is attracted to yin—ideological, intellectual, invisible things—should seek the greatest yin: infinity. If he lacks this greatest dream, he is not a true man. Woman, attracted to yang—home, security, jewelry—should seek the greatest yang, a man who seeks infinity.

Pregnancy

Those who do give birth should know a few things about natural pregnancy. The common experience of odd tastes during pregnancy is natural; it is the baby's way of asking for certain foods that it needs. Many women find, to their chagrin, that they cannot eat their usual food. If you are pregnant and have strong desires for unusual food, follow them, but moderately and with discretion.

A woman's face is usually clear and clean, because she

discharges excess every month during menstruation. When she is pregnant, her face often becomes unclear and dark, especially when the baby is male; in this case, her visage may even become boyish and harsh. She becomes mentally sensitive and easily upset at this time, and she should protect herself a little. Since pregnancy is a yang condition, there is not much excess yin in her system; the hair often gets thinner, and the eyebrows shorter. This is another reason why she craves yin foods. It is difficult to determine pregnancy simply by lack of menstruation, however, for simply changing eating habits can do this.

Man is free of these things, but nothing he can do will ever compare with this experience. The joy of giving birth is hundreds of times greater than anything he knows. Man carries his dream, but woman carries the universe within her. He must seek the universe outside himself. If we discover what dream is, we will know what man is.

Where is Love?

Because most people do not realize that they are living in the infinite, eternal world, they judge and act in the relative world of change. In this world, everything turns into its opposite. Thus, hate becomes love, and love becomes hate. On the sentimental level, we are sad, so we seek; seeking, we take, enjoy, and forget; forgetting, we become sad again. On the sensory level, we hunger, seek, take, satisfy ourselves, forget, and become hungry again. Our happiness is momentary and ephemeral. Between satiety and desire, love and hate, we follow a cyclic, or rather, a spiral pattern of attraction and repulsion. Hate creates sadness, so we seek love; but love turns into hate and the spiral continues.

We are limited to this dualistic, unfree existence only by our arrogance. The highest medicine exists to cure this condition, which is at once the root and flower of "disease." To cure this takes a minute or a lifetime. This is the "devil," or Lucifer. Modern civilization is based on systems of competing arrogance. It is born out of fear, which is, in turn, produced by animal food. Even if one is ignorant, he will be very happy if he has no arrogance.

Since most judge in the relative world, they think that love is a problem of the body. This is the cause of their unhappiness. In this world, everything is constantly changing, so they go from one partner to another, never finding security and permanence. Many are now experiencing great despair, because they can find nothing stable in love. They are only gambling—which is fine for card games and commerce, but not for love. Those who think that love should be sought in the infinite realize that it is a problem of the spirit; they fall in love first, and physical love follows as one of the results. For such people, love can last a long time. You are free to choose whether you have love that changes or is permanent.

Kitchens

If you are buying a home, how do you judge? Do you look for a large, spacious living room, or a luxurious, comfortable bedroom? This is a good test of your understanding of life and order. If you really know what to look for, you will choose a house with a good kitchen.

How can we explain this? Let us begin with nature. Soil, air, stars, wind, water, and trees are condensed into grains and vegetables, the food we eat. Food is the symbolic essence of nature. We eat this concentrated form of our environment and make our life. Our food comes from nature to our kitchen, and is then distributed to the members of the family; from it they build up their ability to adapt to nature. In this journey of return, the kitchen is solidly in the center, just as the midbrain is the center of our nerve impulses. If the kitchen is good, the person who eats from it becomes a large star with many satellites; he has friends, children, a good wife. If the food is of lesser quality, he may have children but no friends, and if it is very poor he must die.

Your life is decided in the kitchen. Whether you have many children and friends, or grow sick and die, everything begins here. If we see a messy kitchen, we see that the man's home is chaos; no matter what he says, what his achievements are, he and his family are disorderly. Many young people, in buying a home, concentrate on the bedroom, but their thinking is completely backward. The kitchen is something like a womb, because it creates life. Other rooms can be cleaned less often, if necessary, but this room should be cleaned at least once a day.

Contracts

When our judgment becomes higher, we see things in completely different ways. Many things that seem normal in our daily lives begin to look unusual and strange. What, for instance, is the purpose of a marriage contract? It seems so surprising and foolish, yet most accept it without question. This has never been adopted in the Orient. What is the meaning of a marriage that must be sealed with one of these? A person must feel very uneasy with a contract of this sort riding over her head, for she must know that she might violate it at any moment! If our marriage is unconditional, we can relax. A contract exists to be broken; it is a sign of mutual distrust. But paper is so fragile; why do people rely on it? The mentality that we see here is very strange--it is a sign of mental illness.

If you have a contract marriage, you must imagine it will be broken someday. If your prospective partner insists on this custom, it might be better if you did not marry. He may trust you sentimentally and emotionally, but he does not really trust you in his heart. This contract, which exists as an agreement between a man and woman, has many parallels: laws, which are made between people and governments; treaties, which are made between nations; and doctrines, which are made between man and his so-called God. All of them are nothing but expressions of distrust. They are the outcome of the egocentric, exclusive mentality that thinks, "I am right, but you may not be." They can exist only between unfree people.

What is Marriage?

What then is marriage? It has nothing to do with going to a church, it is nothing that anyone else can do at all. The meaning of marriage is to make two people's blood into one. This is accomplished by eating the same food and by sexual contact. By intercourse, we exchange fluids which are nothing more than a changed form of blood, and our physical condition, as a result, becomes very different. Because of this, you should be very careful whom you select as a partner—and you should be careful of your own condition. Marriage is, simply put, a form of blood transfusion.

Today, sexual intercourse without love prevails. This is very strange—there is no emotional satisfaction, just automatic sex: we might call this "love of automation." To make love is to change your destiny; if you are not selective, you are giving yourself up to an unknown direction.

The theory that supports this activity is very interesting. It argues that by wide sexual experience one can form higher judgment for selecting a husband or wife. The truth is, if anything, just the reverse. If you can accept physical contact without love you are sparating your mentality from your physique. You are already mentally ill. A naturally healthy person will become selective as a matter of course. Our recommendations are not negative, however; we do not urge anyone to make themselves virtuous, but rather higher, enjoying greater day-to-day happiness and simplicity.

Here are some conditions for a happy marriage. First, eat the same food; second, share the same economy. This is very important; if separate bank accounts are maintained, this condition is violated. Third, the couple should share the same dream, want to have the same kind of life. If you are not satisfying any one of these, your marriage is not perfect. Children should follow naturally from this union, but if they do not, this is no reason for considering your marriage a failure; if you are childless, you can take care of and help other people's children.

To achieve these conditions, both man and wife need

health and gratitude. They need to become grateful both to each other and to others. A man also needs a big dream and the ability to pursue it; his wife needs an understanding of his dream, because she is creating it through her cooking and orderliness in the home.

Love

With these things in mind, we can answer our question. This, then, is a practical, simple, yet all-embracing definition which everyone can understand and use. It is, of course, our own opinion, which you can change and interpret as you wish. Love, for a man, means "I will eat your food." For a woman, love means, "I will follow your dream."

The marriage vow means that a couple will share the same food. By doing this, their blood becomes one; then they can understand each other, have the same dream, and be free of quarrels. This is the most realistic, the most practical, meaning of life. By this, we can judge the depth of a man's love; if he says, "I love you," but eats out often, his love is not real and will soon fade. As long as he eats the same food as his wife, his love will not change. Love is not sacrifice, as many believe, but this very simple, practical sort of sharing.

We can extend this love to include the whole world. When you distribute the macrobiotic way of eating, you can love millions of people. Many religious leaders have taught that we should love everyone without discrimination, but they do not give the practical way of doing so. Love means eating according to the same principles; without this, all words are in vain, and people cannot understand each other because their love is different.

In this universe, there are these opposite things: yin and yang. Man is active, or was; woman is, or was, passive. Thus, they are attracted to each other and complete one another. We can observe this same attraction among the elements. Hydrogen, for instance, is yang, and oxygen is yin. Their difference is very great, so they are attracted and produce water.

If both parties are yin, if man is gentle and timid, this attraction will not be great. Though it remains a possibility, it may take a long time. Another factor is needed in order to effect this combination. If we want to combine copper (yin) and oxygen (yin), we will find that they are never attracted to each other at natural temperatures. By adding heat, we can bring them together. Here we have added a yang factor to combine two yin elements. The same procedure can be used in the world of love. Time, for instance, is yang. Pressure will work well too; if a yin man is encouraged by his friends, or if the draft board begins to write him letters, he is more likely to get married. Another yang method is to bring another male into the picture, in order to produce competition. The best way, of course, is to alter his biological condition by changing his food.

Another sort of combination can be sought between yin and yang. Carbon and hydrogen (both yang) are difficult to combine until a yin factor is used—ultraviolet rays. So if a woman is too yang, a man can take her to a nightclub, listen to soft music, drink, buy her perfume—all yin.

Higher Judgment

Once we have established order in our personal lives, by applying the laws of change, we can begin to widen our dream and our love to embrace the world. The same pattern that we observed between elements and men and women works on this scale. Between two yin nations, there will be no war; both will be peaceful. A yang nation and a yin nation will not fight, either; but two yang countries can be expected to clash, as we can easily observe today. So, for peace, we must introduce a yin factor. Vegetable food and our cosmology can bring peace in a positive, natural way; or we can employ fear, sugar, and more electrical entertainment, a course that will lead to disintegration.

Now, time is very critical. We are facing the possibility of destruction by fire; to combat this yang force, we need a yin component of good quality. Instead of using fire for technology, we should find ways to employ low temperatures. We have managed to transmute the atom at low temperatures (see *Other Dimensions*, by Michio Kushi, Avery Publishing Group, 1992--ed), and we should extend this principle to cover everything in our culture. This is very urgently needed; those who dedicate themselves to this problem will prepare the way for the millennium.

Our methods of solving today's problems are simple, unified, practical, and capable of endless applications. We can bring harmony on a personal, global, or chemical level with the same principles and techniques. You can conquer the whole world by your ideas and dreams, which are beyond the struggling balance of powers that governs the relative world. Just as Locke and Hume developed the idea of democracy, just as Marx, Lennin, Jesus, and Buddha have had millions of followers, including most of the people who are alive today, we can bring real changes if we develop our dream.

The relative world is the field for men and women, but the absolute, infinite world is beyond this: this is the real field of humanity. If you want to win a true victory, you must win here. As long as you continue to search for money, you must continue to discharge it, to surrender; when you master this level you can join the several hundreds of champions that have appeared in the past few thousand years. If you have a big dream, become a winner in this field, become higher than the champions that have come out so far, for all of them have failed; one of the reasons that we still put them in the top ranks of humanity is nothing less than our own laziness.

Raise your judgment and expand your capacity. By always changing, you broaden yourself and embrace more. Great polarity between parents makes for a large capacity; if our mother ate cereals, which are the broadest food, our capacity can be even larger. By exposing ourselves to extremes of heat and cold, happiness and misery, environment and activity, we can develop our capacity without limit. In this way, we can discover new kinds of love, and we can raise all of humanity with us.

19
Self-Consultation

You can test your flexibility by seeing how far back your fingers will bend. If they cannot move ninety degrees, you are, to some extent, limited in your adaptability. Environmental conditions do not bother someone whose health is good. If you eat well, you can enjoy anything. We cannot blame others for our condition. Every factor that influences our health is secondary to food.

Look in the mirror and observe the condition of your eyes. Are there any blood vessels or spots noticeable? This is a sign that your organs are tired and malfunctioning. The areas of discoloration indicate the particular organs. Bloodshot, dots, or discoloration in the upper part of the eye-white (above the iris) are a sign of potential trouble in the brain; while markings or discoloration in the lower portion of the eye-white show possible trouble in the kidneys and sexual organs. Notice that the organs in the upper body are indicated in the upper, most yin area of the eye, and organs in the lower body appear in the lower, most yang region of the eye.

You can divide the eye into sections and diagnose the entire body by yin and yang. If you have beauty marks, moles, or freckles on your skin, this means that you are trying to discharge excess you have eaten by mobilizing the surface of your body. A beauty mark in a sign of a past sickness, its location showing the organ affected. Moles, signaling excess protein, can be removed by good eating. Heavy suntans and freckles are usually excess sugar (yin) being attracted to the sun (yang).

You should not have pain in any part of your body. If you are tender or tired in some spot, then you have weakened one or several of your organs through bad eating. Pinch the junction between your thumb and index finger between the bones; if there is a pain, your intestines are bad. Tired shoulders are also a sign of tired intestines. The arches of the feet are connected to the digestive organs; if they are tired or fallen, these organs are in poor condition.

Blinking more than three times per minute, talking while sleeping, and dreaming are signs of beginning mental illness. The best indication of our condition is our ability to accept everything and give everything without question. If there is anything we fear, we are already mad. Human beings are the last development in this universe; they cannot be destroyed, unless they lower their condition and allow themselves to become open to destructive forces and bacteria.

Habits

There is an Oriental proverb that says, "Even a perfect person has at least seven habits." In other words, there is no perfect person. Our habits reveal much about our character and condition. Here are some habits and their causes:

1. Foot tapping—animal food.
2. Scratching the head—the person feels excess in this place, so he tries to scratch it out. By yangizing a certain place, he can often remember something he has forgotten. Water, fruits, and fats are frequent causes. Nose scratching is very similar.
3. Covering the mouth when talking or laughing—the person is often a big eater, ashamed to show his mouth.
4. Crossing the legs one way often—bad intestines.
5. Arms clasped behind back—bad kidneys, caused by overdrinking.
6. Crossing the arms in front—bad lungs, caused by sugar and fruits
7. Frequently making interjections in speaking—indigestion, making both speech and the functioning or the organs unsmooth.
8. Swinging one arm more than the other while walking—his father and mother were very unlike each other in their conditions when he was conceived.
9. Reading on the toilet—indigestion (a bowel movement should not take more than a few minutes).

10. Muttering to yourself—extremes of both yin and yang.

Every habit has a cause, and they can all be corrected by good eating.

The words "know thyself" were inscribed on the entrances of ancient temples. This self-reflection is the best form of knowledge, and the most practical. To the extent that we are not truly healthy, we are not yet free.

Changing Your Condition

The strongest plant takes a long time to grow. The greatest resistance develops from struggling against coldness and difficulties. If you want instant, impressive results, you are looking in the wrong direction. On the other hand, if you are ready to take a long, slow, but steady way, you can be your own doctor and change yourself into whatever you would like to be.

Our bodies have to make adjustments and eliminate accumulated debris while making a transition from a diet rich in sugar and animal food to one based on grains and vegetables. Americans, especially, should adopt this philosophy of gradual change. An old Chinese proverb says, "To learn to be industrious takes three years; to learn to be lazy takes only three days." Expansion is rapid, but contraction takes time. If you have damaged your body with drugs, you should be especially careful and eat widely for the first few years you are following the way of eating.

In order to adapt to daily changes in your environment and in your own body, you need to be flexible. A rigid dietary regime cannot take special circumstances into account. You need to know when you are becoming too yang or too yin and be prepared to make the appropriate balance.

Some people who have adopted a strict diet of 100 percent grains, plenty of salt, and as little liquid as possible discovered this for themselves, often with unfortunate results. They developed the extreme yang symptoms that occurred among the British sailors who had scurvy. They could have changed this simply by taking a more yin diet (less salt, more liquids and fresh and cooked vegetables). Since they had been taking drugs, without exception, their bodies were not ready for such a drastic change in diet.

How can you tell when you are becoming too yang or too yin? Everyone has special symptoms which he must discover. In general, we tend to be active, then aggressive, and then attacking, cruel, or irritable when we are becoming yang; sensitive, then thoughtful, and finally confused and withdrawn when when we are too yin. Each of these changes into its opposite, however, and the overly yang person can become extremely tired, the overly yin person, accusing and complaining.

Our condition is always changing. We cannot find a balance that will endure forever. We must become more and more flexible, ready to adapt to new demands, if we are to find true health.

A cosmetic dealer, who was visiting Hong Kong, was surprised at the vitality of his rickshaw driver and inquired about his daily diet. He found that this man, who could pull a cart all day, lived on nothing but rice and vegetables. This is not food for "quick energy," but for endurance. Life is like a marathon; if you start out slowly, you can finish the race, while others who start too quickly drop out.

Troubles Coming Out

After you begin eating well, troubles start coming out one by one from deep inside the body. For instance, a person who had cured tuberculosis several years before may suddenly start to cough after several months of eating well; this is a recapitulation of his past history, as the excess inside his body begins to be discharged. Menstruation and sexual desire may diminish or stop completely for awhile, because the organs necessary for life are attended to first. During this process, the blood that nourishes the peripheral organs or that is discharged in menstruation is concentrated in the more central organs such as the liver.

Pregnancy

When a woman becomes pregnant, she develops a very yang condition. The blood she usually discharges each month, which maintains her yin condition, is retained in her body. Often her tastes in food change, especially in the first three months Some women lose all desire for brown rice and crave more yin types of food. If this happens to you, don't feel guilty and try to control your eating intellectually. Follow your desires with moderation and enlarge your diet somewhat. Azuki beans are especially recommended, and can be eaten often.

Restoring a Youthful Condition

Those who follow the way of eating look very young and alive. If you began at the age of twenty, you may look about five years younger; thirty years, seven years younger; forty, ten years; and fifty, up to fifteen years younger. This is often misleading, for it is only the physical age that diminishes; thinking and spiritual age actually become older.

The value of eating this way really becomes evident late in life. Since human beings are yang, it is easy to abuse the intake of yin foods. We are yang when born, and take yin to grow; after the age of twenty-four, when we achieve a balance, we must be careful to avoid extremes. Many continue to take yin foods until they finally exhaust the stock of yang given to them by their mother during her period of pregnancy. Such people maintain their health until the age of forty or fifty, and then begin to deteriorate. If you continue to eat well, your health will continue to improve while others start to decline.

You cannot blame anyone else for your condition. You must realize this before you can change yourself. If you have suffered at the hands of others, it is because you weakened yourself sufficiently to allow it to happen. You cannot blame your parents for your condition, because you chose your parents to make your body. Respect for them is the first qualification for becoming happy and free.

We must change our attitude toward life and root out the mentality that blames others before doing anything else. We must first see justice, the whole view. The inability to see this is arrogance, the sickness of modern humanity. The purpose of good eating is not to cure sickness symptoms, but to cure this exclusivity.

Fear, which is the cause of exclusivity, is the product of generations of disorderly eating. If our food is unbalanced, our view of life will be unbalanced. If we are too yang, we fear yang--competition and power. Yin people fear advice, women, ideas, or religions. In our self-reeducation, we can free ourselves without the aid of institutions, conceptions of education or science. When we were born and began to be bound by restrictive conceptions, we lost this creative ability.

At his last supper, Jesus asked his disciples to partake of his flesh and blood, to make him a part of them and grow even higher. This is the true purpose of education. Any master who cannot make others higher than himself fails. When you have an experience, learn from it and graduate yourself from that viewpoint. Not only is it possible to grow, but human beings can grow infinitely. If only ten were to raise themselves a little higher, the world could be changed. When one becomes happy, everyone is happier; and the way to achieve this is by following the way of eating.

20
What is Dream?

Row, row, row your boat
Gently down the stream
Merrily, merrily, merrily, merrily
Life is but a dream.
—Old English Folk Song

What is it that we call "dream?"

How difficult it can be to explain something. Theories and concepts are so limited and changeable, as is all learned knowledge. For example, what evidence of your own do you have, barring scientific knowledge, that the world is round? In the 1930s, a scientist "proved" that it is shaped like a saucer and demonstrated effectively that we are living inside. No one could disprove this theory at that time. Mathematically, it took everything into account.

Theories are very interesting. This is but one example of many. Many people believe in gravity, for instance, an idea that has only been popular in the last few hundred years. How limited this concept of gravity seems when we see a larger picture! Until the time of Galileo and Copernicus, people thought the earth was flat. When they suggested that we may be living on a round ball, they were threatened. A hundred years from now the idea of gravity may seem as antiquated as the concept of a flat earth.

The Western mentality tends to confuse "theory" with "principle." This is a big problem. Einstein's theory, for example, is not a principle at all but a hypothesis. The law of Archimedes, one of many which has been respected since the time of the Greeks, is actually a theory and not a principle or a law. Some day opposite theories will be developed, the scientific world will be shaken, and a new orthodoxy will result.

Why are such hypothetical theories considered principles? This is a very strange aspect of the Western mentality. Hypothetical and temporary theories are actually techniques. The principle of democracy developed by Hume, Locke, and others, is actually not a principle but a technique or technology.

To the Oriental, a principle is something immortal and unchangeable, something which cannot be ignored at all; something universal, permanent, beyond time and space. Western "principles" are technologies because they are always changing. There are actually no proper words to express the things which are immortal. Of course we can say "God," or "God's law," but it is questionable that most people grasp the idea that this law is unchangeable. Even God is considered to be something vincible. Two or three years ago there was a flurry of propaganda declaring that "God is dead." A reaction proclaimed that "God is still alive." Does the Western mentality include the concept of something invincible and immortal? Frankly, most of the people living in the West today do not know eternity.

What kind of life does this produce? There is a great difference between those who know eternity and those who do not. Every detail of life is changed. Language provides a good example. English is very efficient for business purposes and speedy human relations, but it is very lacking when we want to express our mentality, such as sentimentality or emotions. When a husband and wife talk to each other, for example, they use the same words. In the Orient, and especially in Japan, the men's and women's languages are very different. Since the female's language is very charming and polite, it is very difficult for her to fight with a man.

The real uniqueness of Western languages is a striking lack of respectful words and expressions. In Japanese, "O" or "Go," childlike words which express respect, are often used as prefixes. A meal is "Go-han," and instead of saying, "How is your house?" they say, "How is your respectful house?" Here are some more examples:

Rice - O-Kome
Side dish (vegetables) - O-Sai
Soup - O-Siru
Mountain - O-Yama
Water - O-Mizu
Weather - O-Tenki
Navel - O-Heso
Sickness - Go-Byoki
Address - Go-Ju-Sho
Foot - O-Mi-Asi
House - O-Taku
My Father - Chi-Chi
Your Father - O-Chi-Chi-Ue
Navel - O-Heso

Why did the Far Eastern people develop such a different

mentality? The English and American way is much more effective, speedy, and simple, while the Oriental manner is more complicated. A movement arose to simplify the Japanese language after the war and pattern it more on the model of the Romance tongues. Some people opposed this simplification, feeling that if these seemingly unnecessary expressions were dropped it would be difficult to communicate many things. Mr. Ohsawa wanted to simplify Japanese when he was in his late twenties and devoted himself to Esperanto and other proposals. When he was approaching fifty, he abandoned these ideas. "I have tried to simplify Japanese," he wrote, "but I have learned, through experience with English and French, that with these languages we cannot express delicacy of mentality."

Today, of course, most Eastern people are using these expressions just as slaves. The intention of the ancient people who made these seemingly inefficient expressions, however, is worthy of thought. They paid respect to even the smallest daily objects. Everything was so wonderful to them. A very simple pair of chopsticks, for example. These have been cut and polished by someone and handle many kinds of food in various ways. They seem so wonderful. Our navel, this strange little thing in the center of our belly; the more we see it, the stranger it seems. One grain of rice seems to have some mystery which we cannot totally understand. Perhaps hundreds of people have worked and thousands of years have passed to bring this here. They felt the wonder of nature, the wonder of things, the wonder of people, the wonder of everything; they wanted to use words showing their respect and admiration.

These ancient people who made the original language were living in the middle of the world of wonders. Whatever they saw, whatever they thought, they were always grateful, excited and curious. They were something like children. Jesus said, "Unless you become as children, you cannot enter the Kingdom of Heaven." In comparison to this wonder, they felt small, ephemeral, and vain. Because of this they started to use words to show their respect with every sort of noun, adjective, or expression.

It is difficult to understand this mentality and language unless you actually live with the traditional people. You can understand it, though, if you have been eating well for some months or years. Perhaps some stories would help to explain.

The Mysterious Hit-O-Sai

Baseball has become an increasingly popular sport in Japan. Young and old join their local teams or watch the professional leagues which were revived after the war. One day, thousands had come to see a pitcher who was famous for his strikeout record. For the sake of entertainment, seven people were to be selected out of the audience to take their turn at the plate with a $1,000 prize offered to anyone who could make a hit against this pitcher.

Among the volunteers one stood out in particular. He was wearing a rough, unpolished, old style mountain gown and looked something like an uncle of the hippies. His turn came after all the others had failed. By this time the excitement of the audience was at its peak. This strange man had come to the game out of curiosity and had been picked out at the gate by the ticket collectors as a joke. Although he had no idea what was going on, he stood at the plate without complaining. The famous pitcher wound up and delivered: there was a loud crack and the ball streaked into the far stands for a home run. The audience went wild. The champions who had been sitting and joking in a leisurely way, were dumbfounded. The mountain batter was awarded $1,000.

Two of these champions had followed him after the audience left, determined to find out who he was. In his small apartment they asked him where he had learned about baseball and found that he knew nothing about it at all. He had come simply because he had never seen a game. "Would you come again tomorrow? We would like to know—your home run was so—something strange. Please come."

The next day, between games, three famous pitchers tried to strike him out. Every ball streaked into the far stands. The champions and managers became pale. They had tried themselves for many years and now this strange man, who knew nothing of baseball, hit home runs every time.

They began to question him in earnest. It seems that this man was the descendant of a famous swordsman, Hit-O-Sai, a Sennin who lived five hundred years before. He had developed a famous technique and hid himself away in the deep mountains. His descendants had remained there, passing down his teaching until now. This man was the last of their line.

Now the newspapermen started to get excited. This man had been trained to repulse stones or weapons since he was young; after learning such a technique, a home run would certainly be a childish accomplishment. The team became anxious to employ him, confident that with his abilities, they could never lose.

Finally the Hit-O-Sai signed up. He was made a pinch hitter since he didn't know any of the details of baseball. Whenever the bases were loaded or the situation was tense, he would be sent to the plate and he always delivered a home run. The stands were packed just to see him in action. Other teams felt like giving up and the pitchers tried to throw him balls. One man, however, expressed his frustration by trying to pitch directly at the new star. The Hit-O-Sai did a quick dance, changed around, and the ball hit the catcher and knocked him down instead. The audience roared and the fame of this mountain man continued to grow.

One day an American team came to Japan. Their pitcher was known as one of the best in history. As expected, he struck out most of the Japanese batters. By a stroke of luck, the Japanese team managed to make two runs; the score stood 2 - 2, with men on first and second. At this moment, the Hit-O-Sai was called to bat. The stands trembled with loud excitement. The manager of the Japanese team became pale; this was a great American professional and his delivery was totally different. What if the Hit-O-Sai should fail? His popularity would certainly be spoiled.

The first ball came. The Hit-O-Sai swung and missed and the thousands in the audience all stood up. The second pitch came: strike two! A silent reverberation shook the stands. The pitcher began to wind up for the third pitch when the Hit-O-Sai suddenly raised his hand in a gesture to stop. He walked to the dugout and emerged a few moments later wearing a blindfold. As he strode towards the plate, the American pitcher looked desperately to his manager for directions. The signal came: "No mercy. Kill him."

The pitcher threw his fastest curve. The Hit-O-Sai sent it screaming into the far bleachers for a home run. By wearing a blindfold, he had been able to achieve the utmost quietness and concentration.

Intuition

Mr. Ueshiba was the originator of Aikido, perhaps the most profound martial art in the world today. He was a friend of Mr. Ohsawa and developed his understanding through years of good eating and endless searching. Now, in his old age, he is still on the mats early every morning to teach, defending himself against several men twice his size at one time.

One day, Mr. Ueshiba challenged his best disciples, inviting them to attack him at any time. These students were fifth, sixth and seventh dan judo masters who had studied Aikido for several years. They knew that he was very alert and wanted to find the best time of the day to surprise him. Finally they decided to rush him when he was eating, just at the moment when he was lifting his chopsticks to his mouth. This, they reasoned, should certainly be one time when his attention would be distracted. But whenever one of the disciples was about to make a move to attack, Mr. Ueshiba would suddenly look directly at him. They gathered to confer again. One of them suggested that they surprise him when he was sitting in the washroom. But when they opened the door to rush him, he was standing, facing the door, waiting for them.

Mr. Ueshiba was ready and waiting whenever they tried to attack him. This is the kind of intuition he had acquired through years of eating well. Not only could he sense any kind of attack, but he also showed supernatural sensitivity. One day he surprised a disciple when he told him that he seemed to sense his uncle wondering somewhere. This uncle had died several years ago and the family had been too poor to do anything for him at the time of his memorial just several days before.

There were many men like Mr. Ueshiba in ancient China and Japan. There was one Buddhist monk, the priest of a family temple, who died about fifteen years ago. The villagers would call him to their homes to read whenever someone died. When they arrived to ask him to come, he would often be dressed and waiting for them. This happened so often that the villagers finally asked him how he knew that they were coming. "When a person dies, I feel it," he explained. "In this temple, if it is night, some kind of spirit or wind passes through. I feel it when I am sleeping and so when you come in the morning, I am ready."

Mr. Ohsawa admired Henry David Thoreau very much. On one of his last trips to the United States, he visited Walden Pond and saw the spot where he had built his small cabin. Then he went down to the pond and, kneeling on the bank, sipped some water from his cupped hands. Respectfully he said, "Thank you, Thoreau." ("Thoreau-san, arigato.") His mentality at that time was that he was actually meeting Thoreau. He was appreciating this man whom he admired, a man who remained there as a beautiful memory.

The Hit-O-Sai, Mr. Ohsawa, the monk-there are many examples like this-were living in a world which has no borderline between life and death.

The Way of Eating

The lowest level of eating is without order, chaotic eating, following the demands of convenience and mechanical appetite. For us, this is out of the question.

Second: eating to make yourself healthy. Our way of eating starts from here.

Third: eating to prevent yourself from becoming unhealthy.

Fourth: eating to develop yourself into a higher or better

person.

Most of our friends are eating on the second, third and fourth levels. However, our way of eating does not stop here.

Fifth: eating according to your purpose. This is the beginning of freedom; until we reach this point, we are concerned with health. If you would like to write a book in thirty days, eat in order to accomplish this desire. If you would like to invent something, if you want to be a nice wife or have a good baby, eat accordingly. Whatever you set as your purpose, change your eating to accomplish it.

Sixth: eating to eliminate life and death. In other words, eating to erase the difference between life and death.

A young boy went to see his grandmother's funeral. She was sitting in her coffin, the skin of her eighty-four year old face was almost transparent, dressed in cottons and white linens. Everyone gathered around and someone told her, "This is our last meeting. Please go peacefully on your long travel." The eldest said, "See, your child and grandchild have come to say goodbye." Just at that moment, very fresh red blood came from her mouth, staining the white linen brilliantly. "She knew," some of the people murmured through their tears. "She couldn't say, so she sent a sign." The young boy only knew that something amazing had happened. The coffin was nailed down and lowered into position.

Traditional homes in Japan had small shrines which were used for worship in the morning and evening. These people were living with the memory of dead people. It was quite natural for Mr. Ohsawa to say, "Thoreau-san, thank you." He erased this borderline between life and death. If you eat toward this direction now, your life will become changed. In your everyday life you can see that while you are living, you may be dying, for everyone is disappearing and vanishing away. The ephemerality of life, and yet the permanency of life, we can realize in our daily living. What would happen then? Our desires, what we would like to do to support ourselves or to achieve our dream, and everything else would have a totally different meaning. You are living with dead people as well as live people; you can always talk with them and, sooner or later, you will join their category.

What is Dream?

Now what is your definition of dream? Our stories have been preliminaries to this question.

Everyone knows the answers to questions like this, but few can express themselves. If this is your case, you have hardening of the arteries and your cerebral cells and muscles are also hard. Perhaps you have an image in your mind's eye but cannot express it. If so, you are somewhat crippled; your communicating and interpreting machine is stuck or out of order. This condition is actually a form of stuttering, even if your words flow smoothly. Long winded explanations, excuses, and lack of conviction are symptoms of this common sickness.

Who dreams? If you think that your body is the subject of this dream, you are walking on the street upside down. The subject of dream and memory is infinity itself; infinity is projecting dream or memory through our body.

But most important, what do you do when you see this dream? People are very different in this respect. Some do not try to achieve it at all; some try, but in the most ineffective way possible. One example is the person who feels that he must make plenty of money before starting to do the thing he really wants. The third type of person begins to achieve his dream immediately. The better his health, the faster he translates this dream into reality.

When people reach old age, they begin to see that our life is a dream, for they realize that they might die any day. Usually, they begin to radiate joy. What if you had this feeling while you were young? What if you knew the ephemerality of life and death now and lived accordingly?

Resources

The One Peaceful World Society is an international information network and macrobiotic friendship society founded by Michio Kushi. Membership is $30 year for individuals ($40 outside of the U.S. and Canada) and $50 for families and benefits include the quarterly *One Peaceful World Newsletter*, a free book from One Peaceful World Press, and discounts on books and study materials. To join or for information, please contact: One Peaceful World, Box 10, Becket, MA 01223, (413) 623-2322, Fax (413) 623-6042.

The Kushi Institute is an educational center for macrobiotic and holistic studies. For information on programs, please contact: Kushi Institute, Box 7, Becket, MA 01223, (413) 623-5741, Fax (413) 623-8827.

Recommended Reading

Esko, Edward, *Healing Planet Earth*, One Peaceful World Press, 1996.

Esko, Wendy, *Eat Your Veggies*, One Peaceful World Press, 1996.

Esko, Wendy, *Soup du Jour*, One Peaceful World Press, 1995.

Esko, Wendy, *Rice Is Nice*, One Peaceful World Press, 1994.

Jack, Alex, *Let Food Be Thy Medicine*, One Peaceful World Press, 1994.

Jack, Alex, editor, *Macrobiotic Resource Guide*, One Peaceful World Press, 1998.

Kushi, Aveline and Alex Jack, *Aveline Kushi's Complete Guide to Macrobiotic Cooking*, Warner Books, 1985.

Kushi, Michio, *AIDS and Beyond*, One Peaceful World Press, 1995.

Kushi, Michio, *Basic Home Remedies*, One Peaceful World Press, 1994.

Kushi, Michio, *Standard Macrobiotic Diet*, One Peaceful World Press, 1991.

Kushi, Michio and Edward Esko, *Dream Diagnosis*, One Peaceful World Press, 1995.

Kushi, Michio and Edward Esko, *Forgotten Worlds*, One Peaceful World Press, 1992.

Kushi, Michio and Edward Esko, *Healing Harvest*, One Peaceful World Press, 1994.

Kushi, Michio and Edward Esko, *Holistic Health Through Macrobiotics*, Japan Publications, 1993.

Kushi, Michio and Edward Esko, *Nine Star Ki: Handbook to Oriental Astrology*, One Peaceful World Press, revised 1998.

Kushi, Michio and Edward Esko, *The Philosopher's Stone*, One Peaceful World Press, 1994.

Kushi, Michio and Edward Esko, *Spiritual Journey*, One Peaceful World Press, 1994.

Kushi, Michio and Alex Jack, *The Book of Macrobiotics*, Japan

Publications, 1987.
Kushi, Michio and Alex Jack, *The Cancer Prevention Diet,* St. Martin's Press, 1993.
Kushi, Michio and Alex Jack, *Diet for a Strong Heart,* St. Martin's Press, 1985.
Kushi, Michio and Alex Jack, *The Gospel of Peace,* Japan Publications, 1992.
Kushi, Michio and Alex Jack, *Humanity at the Crossroads,* One Peaceful World Press, 1997.
Kushi, Michio and Alex Jack, *One Peaceful World,* St. Martin's Press, 1986.
Kushi, Michio and Aveline, with Alex Jack, *Macrobiotic Diet,* Japan Publications, 1993.

These and many other books by Michio Kushi and his associates are available by mail order from One Peaceful World Press. Please write for our complete catalogue:

One Peaceful World Press
Box 10, Leland Road
Becket, MA 01223
(413) 623-2322 • Fax (413) 623-6042

About the Author and Editor

Michio Kushi was born in Japan in 1926 and came to the United States in 1949. Over the last forty years, he has lectured and given seminars on health and diet to medical professionals, government officials, and individuals and families around the world, guiding thousands of people to greater health and happiness. He has inspired the creation of the United Nations Macrobiotic Society, led a seminar on AIDS and diet for several hundred medical doctors and World Health Organization representatives in West Africa, and lectured to government officials in China. Founder and president of the Kushi Institute and One Peaceful World, Michio Kushi is the author of numerous books and makes his home in Brookline, Massachusetts.

Edward Esko began macrobiotic studies with Michio Kushi in 1971 and for twenty years has taught macrobiotic philosophy throughout the United States and Canada, as well as in Western and Eastern Europe, South America, Asia, and the Far East. He has lectured on modern health issues and ecology at the United Nations in New York and is on the faculty of the Kushi Institute in Becket, Mass. He is the author of *Notes from the Boundless Frontier, The Pulse of Life,* and *Basics and Benefits of Macrobiotics,* and has co-authored or edited several popular books with Michio Kushi including *Holistic Health Through Macrobiotics.* He lives with his wife, Wendy, and their eight children in the Berkshires.